Life & Death

Ethics Coursebook

Charlotte Vardy

Published by Inducit Learning Ltd trading as pushmepress.com,

Pawlett House, West Street, Somerton,

Somerset TA11 7PS, United Kingdom

www.pushmepress.com

First published in 2013

ISBN: 978-1-909618-34-3

All references from the Qur'an are from the Sahih International translation and from the Bible, the NIV translation.

Links, reviews, news and revision materials available on

www.philosophicalinvestigations.co.uk

With over 20,000 visitors a month, the philosophical investigations website allows students and teachers to explore Philosophy of Religion and Ethics through handouts, film clips, presentations, case studies, extracts, games and academic articles.

Pitched just right, and so much more than a text book, here is a place to engage with critical reflection whatever your level. Marked student essays are also posted.

Contents

Human Life

THE SANCTITY OF LIFE

A belief that human life is sacred is common to the world's major religions. Within the Judaeo-Christian tradition this stems from the idea of Divine Creation. God created man "in his own image" with a purpose.

> *"Then God said, "Let us make mankind in our image, in our likeness ..." So God created mankind in his own image, in the image of God he created them; male and female he created them. God blessed them and said to them, "Be fruitful and increase in number; fill the earth and subdue it." Genesis 1:26-28 (NIV)*

For most Jews and Christians, the connection between human beings and God is in terms of those capacities which are distinctively human - freedom, power, knowledge, understanding, love and goodness. Whereas human beings have these capacities in a limited sense, God is unlimited and perfect.

The Qur'an is clear that Allah created human beings for a purpose, but the idea of creation in the image of God is only really found in the Hadith. For Muslims, the idea that Allah can be understood in terms of human characteristics is controversial as it could challenge the one-ness and unity of God (tawhid).

> *"O mankind, indeed We have created you from male and female and made you peoples and tribes that you may know one another." Qur'an 49:13 (Sahih International)*

GOD'S LOVE

Christians, Jews and Muslims also believe that God knows each one of us and cares about us, making our lives matter to Him.

> *"For you created my inmost being; you knit me together in my mother's womb ... all the days ordained for me were written in your book before one of them came to be."* Psalm 139:13-16

> *"[Allah] Who perfected everything which He created and began the creation of man from clay. Then He made his posterity out of the extract of a liquid disdained. Then He proportioned him and breathed into him from His [created] soul and made for you hearing and vision and hearts ..."* Qur'an 32:6-9

Because of His care for human beings, murder offended God even before he revealed the law, through Moses, Jesus or Mohammed. In Genesis and Qur'an 5:28-32 when Cain murdered his brother Abel, he was exiled, and Sodom and Gomorrah were destroyed for their murderous ways when they did not listen to Lot's warning.

NATURAL LAW

All three major monotheistic traditions have used versions of Aristotelian **NATURAL LAW** to develop their moral teachings. The Christian use of Natural Law is dominated by Aquinas' Summa Theologica, but he was influenced by the reasoning of Islamic scholar **IBN RUSHD**, who suggested that the human mind could identify "basic goods" without revelation, and of Jewish scholar Maimonides, who re-interpreted

Aristotle within a Jewish context. Aristotle argued that a good person flourishes and fulfils their humanity. Good actions contribute to human fulfilment, whilst evil actions cause people to fall short of their potential in one or more ways.

Within Judaism, Christianity and Islam, living, working and reproducing are all essential functions of being human. Choosing to live, work and have children is doing the will of God; choosing not to, or stopping other people, would be a sin against nature, against humanity and against God. Killing or harming human beings is essentially wrong, though there might be exceptions in cases when killing or harming human beings contributes to the greater fulfilment of God's purpose for humanity, such as when we use capital punishment for murderers or when we use military force to prevent civilians from being killed.

MURDER

The Ten Commandments are clear that murder is not allowed, and should be punished by society, not just by God.

> *"You shall not murder" Exodus 20:13*

The Qur'an repeats the laws of the Torah and commands ...

> *"do not kill the soul which Allah has forbidden, except by right." Qur'an 17:33*

Nevertheless, religious views on what actually constitutes murder are less straightforward. Murder is usually defined as the unlawful and intentional killing of another human being. This means that:

- killing in war

- killing in self-defence

- capital punishment

- causing the death of somebody accidentally

- killing an animal

would not usually count as murder. Killing in war, self-defence or as a legal punishment is seen as a **PROPORTIONATE RESPONSE** and **THE LESSER OF TWO EVILS**. Even the Bible is pragmatic enough to see that if people were liberal pacifists more people would be killed or harmed than if an early stand is taken.

INTENTION

Accidental killing, though obviously not good, is not under anyone's control and therefore is not punished to the same extent as intentional killing. Making a distinction between **INTENTIONAL** and **UNINTENTIONAL ACTS** dates right back into the earliest law-codes, such as Exodus 21-22. Today, most scholars agree that people cannot be blamed for deaths or injuries that occur as unintended consequences of good actions. This is known as the **PRINCIPLE OF DOUBLE EFFECT**. Nevertheless, scholars do not agree over how and when this principle might apply.

For example, some scholars argue that the death that occurs more quickly after pain-relieving morphine is injected can be seen as a side-effect, but others say that this is such a well-known side-effect that it cannot be separated out from the intention of the action.

Today, most scholars also accept that there is also a difference between direct and indirect actions, between **ACTS OF COMMISSION** and **ACTS OF OMISSION**. People are more to blame for what they actively and directly do than for what they might fail or omit to do. Killing somebody would generally be worse than allowing somebody to die.

ANIMALS

Killing an animal or other nonhuman being (such as a fish, bird, or plant) is not regarded as morally wrong within mainstream Judaism, Christianity or Islam, because:

1. Human beings were given all the plants, fish, birds and animals to use for food (Genesis 1:26-31, Qur'an 40:79).

2. Nonhuman beings do not have moral status.

   (a) Within Judaism and Christianity only human beings have a God-given and immortal **SOUL**.

   (b) Within Islam Allah created human beings and animals differently; any blurring of the boundary is forbidden as it goes against the will of Allah (Qur'an 55:10). Only human beings were given the responsibility to be caretakers Khalifa of the earth.

   "Then the Lord God formed a man from the dust of the ground and breathed into his nostrils the breath of life, and the man became a living being." Genesis 2:7

Many Jews, Christians and Muslims have been concerned to limit animal suffering where possible, but few question the essential **ONTOLOGICAL DIFFERENCE** between humans and animals. The difficulty comes when science seems to blur the boundaries between what is human and what is animal. Should we really treat an early-embryo as a full human person and a chimpanzee, with all its capacity for suffering and communication, as nothing at all?

New wine in old wine-skins

Developments in medicine have made the process of defining murder, and by implication defining humanity, even more important.

Neither the Bible nor the Qur'an contains specific teaching governing issues such as embryo research, IVF and related fertility treatments, contraception, abortion or euthanasia. Given that:

- Cloned embryos can now be used to harvest embryonic stem-cells, which might be used to treat Parkinson's disease or spinal trauma.

- Doctors can put some human DNA into the embryos of mice or pigs, causing them to grow tissue for transplant or to test human drugs.

- Neonatal Intensive Care Units (**NICU**) are able to save very premature babies, but often they will have severe complications which require long-term hospital care and will have little hope of living long and normal lives.

- Antibiotics and other medical treatments prevent early deaths from illness, accidents or heart-attacks - meaning that more people survive for longer, sometimes with severe disabilities, often to contract and eventually die from cancer or another long-term incurable condition.

- Intensive care enables people in comas or persistent vegetative states (**PVS**), or with "locked in syndrome" to be kept alive for many years without being able to communicate or effect their wishes.

Many Jews, Christians and Muslims want and need guidance on what is and is not acceptable.

RELIGIOUS TEACHING TODAY

Religious authorities develop teachings on the basis of scripture and tradition interpreted within the spirit of general principles such as the Sanctity of Human Life. In practice, this has tended to result in very conservative guidelines on most of these issues, with most religious people being discouraged from condoning embryo research, some forms of IVF and fertility treatments, at least abortofacient methods of contraception, abortion and euthanasia.

In many cases the reason for conservatism in religious teaching comes down to an uncertainty over when human life really begins and ends, over what human life should really be regarded as sacred and accorded moral status, and why.

Nevertheless, this conservatism has led to increasing numbers of religious people choosing to disregard religious teachings:

- Italy has become an international centre for fertility treatment, pioneering IVF for much older women.

- Singapore and Israel have become world-leaders in genetic research.

- Large numbers of Catholic couples are using contraception, including methods which might be abortofacient (causing an abortion).

- In the UK some Islamic couples are using IVF and genetic selection to avoid congenital conditions.

Whilst it is difficult to pinpoint a moment when a human being becomes or ceases to be a person with a morally valuable life and whilst it is difficult to formulate a law which respects individual autonomy but prevents abuse, saying that everything with human DNA is equal and valuable, when this means sacrificing pregnant women or forcing people to suffer prolonged and painful deaths, seems unsatisfactory to many people.

Much of the appeal of **SITUATION ETHICS**, which places the decision making power and responsibility onto individuals, lies in the fact that it offers believers, as well as humanists, a way to balance their respect for the sanctity of human life in general against their respect for the wishes and interests of individuals; it demands that we put people rather than principles centre-stage. Nevertheless, major Churches (as well as most Imams and Rabbis) reject the idea that ordinary people could and should be left to make life and death decisions for themselves; there is just too much scope for letting the heart rather than the head rule.

PERSONHOOD

So what is a human being?

If we focus on **LOOKS** and/or **CAPABILITIES**, there is potential for people who look different or have restricted abilities to be regarded as second-class citizens.

- Is it reasonable to question the humanity or moral status of severely disabled people or brain-damaged people?

- Are people with Downs Syndrome less human than other people?

- How about Ben Parkinson MBE, who survived the worst ever battlefield injuries in Afghanistan? He lost both his legs and sustained more than 40 injuries including brain damage that affected his memory and speech - but still carried the Olympic torch and raises thousands for charity.

If we focus on **DNA** then:

- Questions must be raised about the treatment of "spare" embryos, created in the lab and having no potential to be implanted in a mother and proceed in development.

- All human tissue and even dead people have human DNA; do we give amputated limbs or corpses moral consideration?

- Human genes have been given to mice and pigs, to enable them to grow organs for transplantation. How much human DNA does something have to have in order to qualify as a human being?

- Higher primates share a lot of DNA with human beings. Should we be giving more moral consideration to beings which share more DNA with human beings? (Bear in mind that we share about 95% with mice and 89% with zebrafish).

- Research shows that dolphins and collie dogs as well as primates are able to communicate better than young children and even do basic maths. It is obvious that higher-animals suffer and even mourn and have sophisticated relationships, including with people. Why do we disregard animals whilst giving moral consideration to embryos or people in PVS?

If we focus on **SOCIAL INTEGRATION** there could be a difference between who is accepted as a human being with moral status in one society and another.

- In ancient Sparta newborn babies were left to die on the hillside overnight; only the fittest were accepted.

- In Nazi Germany Jews were locked up in ghettos and camps because they were not accepted as full citizens, or even full human beings.

- In America and South Africa black people were not allowed to integrate; they were kept out of good housing, education, local facilities and jobs and were prevented from voting by law.

- In China female babies are often aborted or even abandoned after birth because people don't want to accept them into their families.

- Does the fact that widows are often rejected by their families and communities in India really mean that widows are less human than other people, that they should be regarded as less important in moral discussions?

PERSONHOOD is a way of expressing a being with moral status, whose life must be counted in moral calculations. It might be equivalent to humanity, but it might be held to exclude some human beings or to include some non-human beings, depending on the criteria it is held to depend on.

The Law and Personhood

In this country legal protection only applies to those **IN BEING**, which means after the point of birth and breathing independently. While there are some laws protecting the unborn, they are specific rather than just being extensions of the general prohibition on murder. In law it is acceptable to kill an unborn child in order to save the life or health of an adult, or to protect the interests of a child - and it is even acceptable to select which of several unborn children to kill. It follows that legally full personhood is associated a degree of independent human existence.

Nevertheless, the point of birth seems **ARBITRARY** when we consider that a 24 week foetus in the womb is not considered to be "in being" whilst a premature baby at the same stage of development in the Neonatal Intensive Care Unit (NICU) is. Ethically, is there really a difference between aborting a 24 week foetus diagnosed with Downs Syndrome and killing a severely disabled pre-term baby in the intensive care unit?

It is clear that there is no easy answer to the question of what a human being is. Drawing distinctions, claiming that some human beings ought to count as more than others in a moral calculation, is fraught with difficulties and yet using a very broad definition, seeing four cell embryos as morally equivalent to adults or those suffering in the last stages of cancer as morally equivalent to healthy teenagers creates problems as well.

Philosophical Views of Personhood

Plato's ideas about the soul are explored in the Phaedo and in The Republic. In the final argument of the Phaedo Socrates states

> *"What is it that, when present in a body, makes it living? — A soul"*

The soul is what brings an organism alive. In Book IV of The Republic Plato suggests that the human soul has three parts - reason, spirit and appetite. We all exist like animals in wanting to eat, sleep and reproduce, but we are capable of more. We can be loyal to friends and family and have an emotional life and, at the highest level, we can aspire to a rational, intellectual life.

For Plato, it is the rational soul which makes human beings unique and morally valuable.

While observing chicks developing inside eggs, Aristotle saw that embryos gradually took form in a process he called **EPIGENESIS**. Aristotle argued that all things, including embryos, have **FOUR CAUSES**.

- **MATERIAL CAUSES** - the basic physical ingredients

- **EFFICIENT CAUSES** - the agents which cause the thing to be as it is

- **FORMAL CAUSES** - the definitions, which define the thing to be as it is

- **FINAL CAUSE** - the end towards which things develop, the purpose of things

For Aristotle women's menstrual blood is the material cause whilst a man's semen is the efficient cause of a new life; women are passive in the process of procreation, whereas men are active. The formal cause of human life is the rational soul, which enables a mass of blood to take a human form.

In *The History of Animals Book VII*, Aristotle explained that male embryos take form around 40 days after conception (their genitalia are present at this stage) but female embryos take 90 days to be **ENSOULED**.

He wrote:

"In the case of male children the first movement usually occurs on the right-hand side of the womb and about the fortieth day, but if the child be a female then on the left-hand side and about the ninetieth day ... About this period the embryo begins to resolve into distinct parts, it having hitherto consisted of a fleshlike substance without distinction of parts ... In the case of a male embryo aborted at the fortieth day, if it be placed in cold water it holds together in a sort of membrane ... If the membrane be pulled to bits the embryo is revealed, as big as one of the large kind of ants; and all the limbs are plain to see, including the penis, and the eyes also, which as in other animals are of great size. But the female embryo, if it suffer abortion

during the first three months, is as a rule found to be
undifferentiated." Part III

For Aristotle all organisms have a **SOUL**, which defines the form of the organism and determines whether it is human, chicken or lettuce. For Aristotle, soul does not suggest any supernatural quality, though human beings are unique and valuable because they possess reason.

For both Plato and Aristotle a person cannot be seen to be a person from conception. Humanity is associated with a human form or with distinctively human capabilities and arrives gradually, but starting sometime after new life itself begins. It follows that an embryo might have a vegetative or animal soul, a foetus might acquire a locomotor or emotional soul after quickening and a child might only later develop a rational soul - maybe not till the teenage years.

It was this interpretation of Greek philosophy that later inspired philosophers such as Thomas Hobbes.

Some Christian scholars understood personhood differently. Drawing on the Hebrew scriptures, which suggest that a soul exists at least from the early stages of pregnancy, Tertullian reminds us that:

"They [John and Jesus] were both alive while still in the womb.
Elizabeth rejoiced as the infant leaped in her womb; Mary
glorifies the Lord because Christ within inspired her. Each
mother recognises her child and is known by her child who is
alive, being not merely souls but also spirits." De Anima XXVI

Continuing,

"We indeed maintain that both [body and soul] are conceived, and formed, and perfectly simultaneously, as well as born together; and that not a moment's interval occurs in their conception." De Anima XXVII

Yet other Christians accepted the Greek distinction between an unformed and a formed foetus, which led to early-stage abortions being tolerated or punished relatively lightly by the Church until the late Middle Ages, despite occasional objections.

This was in part due to the influence of St Augustine, a Platonist and believed that ultimate reality is not physical. The physical world is a partial, limited shadow of a perfect, eternal reality beyond the senses. Augustine was a **DUALIST**, believing that human nature consists of both soul and body. The soul, which is immaterial and immortal and created directly by God, enables human beings to survive death, entering an eternal life.

Augustine was not clear about the origin of the soul or when it came into the embryo. When commenting on the book of Exodus, which appears to make a distinction between "unformed" and "formed" foetuses in the Greek Septuagint (LXX) translation, he wrote that,

"the law does not provide that the act (abortion) pertains to homicide, for there cannot yet be said to be a live soul in a body that lacks sensation." On Exodus 21.22

Though he seemed to condemn those who procure abortions, writing

"Sometimes, indeed, this lustful cruelty ... resorts to such

extravagant methods as to use poisonous drugs to secure
barrenness; or else, if unsuccessful in this, to destroy the
conceived seed by some means previous to birth ..." De Nube et
Concupiscentia 1.17 (15)

Given that it was very difficult to date pregnancies accurately in the Middle Ages **QUICKENING**, the first felt movement of the foetus, came to be seen as the point of ensoulment. Pope Innocent III (d.1216) ruled that abortion before the point of quickening was a less serious sin than it would be after that point.

St Thomas Aquinas was influenced by his readings of St Augustine and Aristotle when he suggested that a person could not really be regarded as a person from conception. For Aquinas ensoulment occurred later on in pregnancy as Aristotle had suggested. This did not make abortion acceptable; killing an embryo goes against natural law in that it prevents it from fulfilling its potential and demonstrates that sexual intercourse has been used inappropriately. Nevertheless, for Aquinas, early-stage abortion is not quite equivalent to murder.

Another strand of Christian thought originated in the writings of Boethius, who wrote that the soul is "the individual substance of a rational nature." (Liber Contra Eutychen et Nestorium 3).

This identification of humanity with the rational, conscious mind became associated with Catholic philosopher Rene Descartes, who famously wrote "I think, therefore I am". Immanuel Kant, who was brought up Lutheran, wrote that:

"the capacity to set oneself an end - any end whatsoever - is
what characterizes humanity (as distinguished from animality)."

The Metaphysics of Morals

Some Christians have always seen **RATIONALITY** as that which makes human beings morally valuable.

During the Enlightenment Thomas Hobbes and John Locke came to understand personhood in terms of **CONSCIOUSNESS**. Hobbes argued that the person can only be seen as a person if their actions are considered, either by other people or reflectively - although this position gives parents absolute power to dispose of over born as well as unborn children (Leviathan Book I, chap. XVI:1 & 10, Elements of Law XXIII:8). John Locke noted that:

"Since consciousness always accompanies thinking, and it is that which makes everyone to be what he calls self, and thereby distinguishes himself from all other thinking things, in this alone consists personal identity." An Essay Concerning Human Understanding

Today, Derek Parfit's definition of personhood and identity is widely discussed. He focuses on **SPATIO-TEMPORAL CONTINUITY UNDER A CONCEPT**. By this reasoning it would be possible to argue that an embryo/foetus in the womb is a stage in a continuous line which includes the adult person. If it deserves respect as an adult it deserves respect as an embryo/foetus because it shares the same identity, if not the same capabilities at all points. As Gillespie stresses in his article "Abortion and Human Rights" there is **NO MORALLY RELEVANT BREAK IN THE BIOLOGICAL PROCESS** of development. As Norman Gillespie stressed in his article "Abortion and Human Rights" (1984), there is no morally relevant break in the biological process of development.

However, like Locke, Derek Parfit (1971) sees **PSYCHOLOGICAL CONNECTEDNESS** as important in establishing personal identity. If a state-of-mind depends on an earlier state-of-mind then it is connected to it. It is not clear that our experiences before birth are connected to our later psychological identities and by this logic it could be that personhood is not established until our brains develop sufficiently to retain even subconscious memories.

Suggesting that personhood depends on capabilities does not necessarily mean that **POTENTIAL PERSONS** should not be treated with respect. Embryos, foetuses and infants might be protected because preventing them from fulfilling their human potential is seen to be wrong. Nevertheless, seeing personhood as dependent on capabilities is often seen as the start of a slippery slope towards devaluing the vulnerable.

For Peter Singer moral status is acquired gradually, after the point of conception and even birth, and depends on capabilities. Human beings are not ontologically different from animals or unique in having moral worth, because higher functioning animals have the ability to suffer, have desires and interests.

For Singer, the only criterion of personhood which makes sense is that of **INTERESTS**. Beings which have interests must have **DESIRES**. For example, it is in the interests of a being which wants to live to be allowed to continue living and can be said to be its **RIGHT** to do so, but it also follows that a being whose desire is to die will not have its interests best served by being prevented from dying. Inanimate objects have neither interests nor rights and lower-functioning animals and human beings, those which have no desires, have neither interests nor rights either.

In *Rethinking Life and Death* Singer suggests replacing five old commandments with five new, more rational moral laws.

1. "Treat all human life as of equal worth" becomes "Recognise that the worth of human life varies".

2. "Never intentionally take innocent human life" becomes "Take responsibility for the consequences of your decisions".

3. "Never take your own life, and always try to prevent others from taking theirs" becomes "Respect a person's desire to live or die".

4. "Be fruitful and multiply" becomes "Bring children into the world only if they are wanted".

5. "Treat all human life as always more precious than any nonhuman life" becomes "Do not discriminate on the basis of species." (Rethinking Life and Death OUP 1994:190-206).

Point 5 is most important. **SPECIESISM** has no rational basis.

Singer asks;

"That many nonhuman animals have interests and welfares is difficult to deny, for they are certainly capable of feeling pain and suffering as well as pleasure and joy. There is no nonreligious reason why the pains and pleasures of nonhuman animals should not be given equal weight with… human beings." Peter Singer, "Taking Humanism Beyond Speciesism"

He suggests that unwanted or disabled babies should be aborted or even killed after birth, that terminally ill people who want to die should be given help and that those in persistent vegetative state or with Alzheimer's could be non-voluntarily euthanised and the money saved in not treating them used to help those whose interests could be better served. Nevertheless, he campaigns against poverty and sees it as a positive duty to help those in need.

On the moral and legal status of abortion, the feminist philosopher Mary-Anne Warren (1946-2010) suggested that:

> *"The traits most central to the concept of personhood are, very roughly, the following: consciousness, reasoning, self-motivated activity, the capacity to communicate, the presence of self-concepts, and self-awareness."*

She argued that abortion is not murder and can, situationally, be a good thing. Differently, the Roman Catholic philosopher John Finnis argued that "the most radically and distinctive human characteristic of all (is) the fact that she was conceived of human parents." There is a "perfectly clear-cut beginning to which each one of us can look back and in looking back see how, in a vividly intelligible sense, 'in my beginning is my end'." (1973:6).

Defining when a person is a person is foundational to most arguments about the morality of abortion, but also of IVF, genetic engineering and euthanasia to some extent.

GOD AND GOOD

Maintaining that human life is sacred and that abortion, euthanasia and embryo research are absolutely wrong, is usually associated with religious groups who believe that human life is sacred because God created it with a purpose. Notwithstanding what this might say about God's nature, most Christian, Jewish and Muslim moral philosophers see what is good as essentially depending on a **DIVINE COMMAND**.

As JL Mackie observed,

> *"'If God is dead, everything is permitted.' Those who have begun by identifying morality with a body of divine commands naturally conclude that if there were no God, there could be no moral rules." (1977:277)*

Those who do not believe in God, and those who believe in God but doubt the special status of scripture, have to justify the natural preference that people show for other people in their decision making in some rational way - and doing so is not straightforward. As Peter Singer remarked,

> *"humanists have on the whole been unable to free themselves from one of the most central of these Christian dogmas: the prejudice of speciesism" (2004:19-21)*

ETHICAL THEORIES AND THE SANCTITY OF LIFE

Although versions of moral systems such as Natural Law, Kantian Ethics and Utilitarianism do not obviously depend on religious beliefs, it is notable that many philosophers just assume that all human beings, and not animals, should have moral status.

Although most philosophers of the Natural Law tradition operate within a religious framework, arguably their systems should work whether or not people accept that God caused human nature to be as it is. Does Natural Law necessarily lead to a belief in the special status of human life? Probably not. It is clear that life is usually a basic good, not just for human beings but for all beings; actions which take or harm any form of life prevent beings from flourishing and are to be discouraged. However, it is impossible to live whilst causing no harm, so in practice damage must be limited to what is **PROPORTIONATE** to the need.

Moral Philosophers such as Louis Jannsens and Bernard Hoose avoid making absolute prohibitions, even on killing, suggesting that actions must be judged in relation to the situation and their consequences. Nevertheless, **PROPORTIONALISM** is rejected by many other philosophers of the Natural Law tradition and by the mainstream Roman Catholic Church, because it places too much responsibility on individuals, causes confusion and is likely to lead to more bad things being done.

For Kant, that other people deserve our respect appeals directly to our reason.

- Although only a free, rational person who chooses to act according to reason every time has absolute value, it is reasonable to treat other people, who may have a "good will" for all we know, with respect.

- Because we respect other people, they have dignity and become ends in themselves, treated as if sacred rather than as possible means to ends like all other animals or things.

- For Kant, human life must be treated as if sacred and never as a means to an end, not because human beings can be known to have a special value but because it is reasonable to suppose that they might have.

People should treat other apparent people as they themselves would wish to be treated.

"Act only according to that maxim by which you can at the same time will that it should become a universal law." Groundwork, 421

Kant agreed with Rousseau that it seems reasonable to give others the benefit of the doubt, being rather generous in who we judge to have the ability or potential to act morally, because it is very easy to underestimate people - and the consequences of doing this are much worse than the consequences of treating a non-moral being as if it was moral.

As Allen Wood puts it:

"there can be no duties whatever to non-human living things, or to the natural world, or to God (or other nonhuman spirits) ... Persons are ends in themselves, while things have value only as means". (2004)

Nevertheless, moral philosophers who have been influenced by Kant have not always appreciated the subtlety of his position. Some have suggested that we respect human beings because we know them to have dignity. Although this is probably not faithful to Kant, it has shaped how Kantian Ethics has developed, so it is probably reasonable to say that many Kantian moral philosophers assume the value of human beings without necessarily arguing for it.

Most versions of utilitarianism just assume that (all) human beings count (equally?) in moral calculations, whereas nonhuman beings do not. Some versions, such as that of Peter Singer, relate this to the generally greater ability of human beings to suffer or the greater range of interests held by most people. This approach might suggest that any human beings who could not suffer, or who could suffer less, or who had fewer or no interests could be counted as less - and any animal which had a higher ability to suffer or which had interests could be counted as more. Other versions reason that giving all human beings equal moral status is justified by the greater good that is caused by doing so than would be caused by not doing so. John Stuart Mill's utilitarianism and modern theories of Rule Utilitarianism are like this.

Virtue Ethics is not in the business of labelling actions good or evil; rather it is all about the long-term effects of actions on peoples' characters. Is harming or killing something with human DNA likely to have more of an effect on somebody's character than harming or killing an animal? Probably. Nevertheless, that does not say that harming or killing an animal does not matter.

KEY TERMS

sanctity of Life - imago dei - personhood - flourishing - speciesism - natural law - proportionalism - situation ethics - divine command - ensoulment - quickening - viability - efficient cause - formal cause - principle of Double Effect

SELF-ASSESSMENT QUESTIONS

1. What do Christians, Jews and Muslims mean by saying that human life is sacred?

2. What is murder? Is abortion murder according to UK law?

3. Explain, using examples, what scholars mean by "the Principle of Double Effect"

4. What is the difference between an act of commission and an act of omission?

5. "A human being is a thinking ape". Discuss the implications of this view for medical ethics.

6. Explain what Plato and Aristotle meant by "soul".

7. Explain why Abortion would still be wrong for Augustine and Aquinas, even if the early-embryo or foetus is not fully human.

8. Do you find the view of personhood held by Hobbes or by Singer most appealing? Why? What are the strengths and weaknesses of this approach in your opinion?

9. Explain why Immanuel Kant thought we should treat other people with respect.

10. Derek Parfit sees psychological connectedness as a symptom of physical completeness; the foetus cannot be seen to be part of a continuous identity until its thoughts are connected. Explore the impact this might this have on his attitudes to abortion, IVF and embryo research - and how he might respond to people who have amnesia or who are in a coma or PVS.

FURTHER READING

- **SINGER, P.** - Rethinking Life and Death, OUP (1994)

- **PARFIT, D.** - Reasons and Persons, Oxford Paperbacks (1986)

- **DWORKIN, R.** - Justice for Hedgehogs, Harvard University Press (2011)

- **LIZZA, J. P.** (ed.) - Defining the Beginning and End of Life: Readings on Personal Identity and Bioethics, Johns Hopkins University Press (2009)

- **WARREN, M.** - Moral Status: Obligations to Persons and Other Living Things, Clarendon Press; New Ed (2000)

- **STEINBOCK, B.** (ED.) - Life Before Birth: The Moral and Legal Status of Embryos and Fetuses, Second Edition, OUP (2011)

Doctor's Dilemmas

Most people are shaped by parents, peers, teachers, law and media in forming their values and opinions. In practice, few people are directly influenced by Natural Law, Utilitarianism or Kantian Ethics, and this includes doctors.

Nevertheless, doctors face increasingly challenging decisions and need clear and consistent ways of making them. **MEDICAL ETHICS** govern doctors' responses to the issues covered in this book, to abortion, euthanasia, IVF and fertility treatment and Genetic Engineering, so it is important to consider what they are, where they come from and how they relate to and compare with religious and philosophical approaches to the same issues.

THE HIPPOCRATIC OATH

The Hippocratic Oath is thought to have been written in about the 5th Century BCE. Part of one version reads as follows:

> *"I will prescribe regimens for the good of my patients according to my ability and my judgment and never do harm to anyone. I will not give a lethal drug to anyone if I am asked, nor will I advise such a plan; and similarly I will not give a woman a pessary to cause an abortion. But I will preserve the purity of my life and my arts. I will not cut for stone, even for patients in whom the disease is manifest; I will leave this operation to be*

performed by practitioners, specialists in this art. In every house where I come I will enter only for the good of my patients, keeping myself far from all intentional ill-doing and all seduction and especially from the pleasures of love with women or with men, be they free or slaves. All that may come to my knowledge in the exercise of my profession or in daily commerce with men, which ought not to be spread abroad, I will keep secret and will never reveal".

Even today many doctors swear a professional oath or otherwise subscribe to a professional code of ethics directly inspired by the Hippocratic Oath. What does it suggest about the values which doctors share and the way in which they approach decision-making?

Firstly, that medical ethics is a secular, professional matter. In ancient times Doctors swore "by Apollo, the healer, Asclepius, Hygieia, and Panacea", but today most codes do not mention God. Rules are generally agreed between professionals as best practice rather than seen as the result of either divine commands or a more general moral philosophy.

The oath concludes

"If I keep this oath faithfully, may I enjoy my life and practice my art, respected by all men and in all times; if I swerve from it or violate it, may the reverse be my lot".

The reward for good behaviour lies in professional respect and the real punishment lies in being repudiated by other doctors. It is still the case that doctors fear being "struck off" the register by their peers far more than being arrested and tried under the general law.

It is also the case that medical ethics demands more of doctors than does the law. For example, it is often not illegal for doctors to have sexual relationships with patients, but it would be seen as a gross breach of medical ethics.

- Some doctors take the Hippocratic prohibitions on abortion and euthanasia very seriously and see that even if they are legal, they cannot **IN CONSCIENCE** be involved in such procedures, simply because they are doctors, irrespective of any religious views they might or might not have.

- Other doctors see their duty to preserve **CONFIDENTIALITY** as more important than any legal obligation placed on them to surrender information which might be of interest to the police.

MODERN MEDICAL ETHICS

There are four key principles, broadly derived from the Hippocratic Oath, which give rise to modern medical ethics:

- The principle of **BENEFICIENCE** - to care for and to benefit patients and to act in their best interests.

- The principle of **NON-MALEFICENCE** - to seek to remove harm from patients: 'Above all, do no harm'.

- The principle of **AUTONOMY** or **SELF DETERMINATION** - to respect the free decisions of patients and to keep them fully informed of the alternatives open to them

- The principle of **JUSTICE** - the obligation to fairly distribute benefits and risks.

The first two of these principles give rise to the **BENEFICENCE MODEL OF MEDICAL ETHICS**, which puts the emphasis on the doctor to decide what is right and sees human life as something of inherent value (sometimes regardless of its quality or the wishes of the patient).

The second two principles give rise to the **AUTONOMY MODEL OF MEDICAL ETHICS** which emphasises the doctor's duties to the patient and the wider community, seeing him or her as serving the greater good, fairness and liberty rather than just prolonging life.

Despite the fact that different models of medical ethics focus more on beneficence or more on autonomy, all four principles are seen to be important and there is often tension between them, which plays out when difficult decisions have to be made.

- Sometimes patients do not seem to know what is good for them, making irrational decisions about their own care. Doctors have to decide whether to ignore the autonomy of the patient in their own best interests, in favour of beneficence.

- Sometimes beneficence (as well as autonomy and justice) pulls against non-maleficence. Acts which cause harm or even death seem medically necessary in order to stop suffering, as when a patient is in such agony that even morphine does not work.

- Sometimes patients are unable to make autonomous decisions. Doctors will then act according to the principle of beneficence, but it is not always easy when continuing treatments seems likely to have been against what the patient would have wanted or what serves the just distribution of resources.

- Sometimes patients request treatment which is very expensive but does not seem worthwhile given the likely benefit, such as some drugs for cancer or Alzheimer's Disease. Doctors have to balance autonomy against justice.

- Similarly, when some patients ask for euthanasia, doctors may see it as a case of balancing the individual patient's autonomy and interests against the wider interests of the vulnerable in society, concluding that allowing individual cases of euthanasia might not serve justice in general.

Furthermore, medical ethics are complicated by confusion over who is the doctor's patient. For example, a pregnant woman can be viewed as one adult patient or as one adult patient and one child patient. What is in the interests of the mother might not be in the interests of the child; to whom is the doctor professionally responsible? Similar problems arise in the cases of children, in cases of conjoined twins or in cases where a dependent adult has a long-term carer.

AUTONOMY AND CONSENT

"An adult patient who…suffers from no mental incapacity has an absolute right to choose whether to consent to medical treatment… This right of choice is not limited to decisions which others might regard as sensible. It exists notwithstanding that the reasons for making the choice are rational, irrational, unknown or even non-existent." Lord Donaldson

In UK Law **COMPETENT** adults are given the autonomy to accept or refuse medical treatments. This sometimes causes doctors concern as it can be difficult to define who should be regarded as such a competent adult, especially when odd and apparently irrational decisions are being made or when a patient is borderline mentally ill, a teenager or childlike in some respect.

Cases involving peoples' religious beliefs are often covered in medical dramas and attract a lot of media attention when they occur.

1. A young Baptist woman who is diagnosed with cancer shortly after becoming pregnant may refuse chemotherapy, because the drugs would definitely harm or cause the death of her child, even when this decision might shorten her life and leave her other children motherless. Should her autonomy be respected?

2. A terminally-ill priest might refuse painkilling medication because Pope John Paul II wrote "praise may be due to the person who voluntarily accepts suffering by forgoing treatment with pain-killers in order to remain fully lucid ... they ought to be able to prepare in a fully conscious way for their definitive meeting with God", (Evangelium Vitae n.65). Should doctors intervene, knowing that the same Pope said that "such "heroic" behaviour cannot be considered the duty of everyone" to prevent the man from enduring appalling suffering because of a peculiar interpretation of his religious beliefs?

A related issue is that of **CONSENT**. In order to preserve the autonomy of patients, it is ethically and legally necessary for doctors to obtain consent for any treatment which they administer. In order for this consent to be valid, it must be **INFORMED**, that is, the patient must be properly aware of the situation, their options and the risks involved.

Nevertheless, it can be difficult to obtain informed consent, given the practicalities of some situations. For example:

1. A young man is rushed to A&E after a car accident. He needs to have a risky operation to stop internal bleeding, but has sustained a head injury as well, which might be affecting his ability to think clearly. Can he consent to treatment, or must the doctors wait for his wife's plane to land?

2. An elderly woman is diagnosed with lung cancer. An operation to remove the tumour will leave her with limited lung-capacity but could extend her life by a few months, as compared with giving her radiotherapy alone. There are significant risks associated with having anaesthetic. She shows some signs of dementia, but has not been diagnosed with Alzheimer's. Is the consent she gives for the operation valid, or should her doctors decide what is in her best interests?

3. A 32 year old woman with Down's Syndrome is brought into hospital from a care-home. She has no known relatives and is suffering from a heart problem. She is very frightened of being in hospital and wants to return to her own room, which is worsening her condition, but if she is not monitored closely her condition might worsen anyway. What should the doctors do? What is in the patient's best interests?

Patients who are younger than 18 or deemed to be incompetent for some reason cannot consent to their own treatment, which must be consented to by a parent, guardian, doctor or even a court.

A particular problem occurs where the parents (or, more rarely, the guardians or doctors) of a patient seem to be making decisions which are not in the best interests of the patient. In these cases doctors can challenge decisions and ask a court to rule on what would be best.

AUTONOMY, INFORMATION AND TRUST

In 2001 Baroness Onora O'Neill gave the Gifford Lectures on the theme of "Autonomy and Trust in Bioethics". O'Neill is a modern Kantian, seeing freedom and rationality as the keys to personhood.

The lectures highlighted a shift in Medical Ethics away from the traditional beneficence model and towards an autonomy model. O'Neill asked why it is that the process of giving patients more information and control makes them less and not more trusting of doctors?

One possible factor is **THE IMPLICATIONS OF AUTONOMY FOR PERSONHOOD**. If autonomy is seen as central to preserving patients' rights it is a step to seeing rights as contingent on autonomy, which might exclude a lot of human beings from full moral consideration.

Another factor is the public **PERCEPTION OF RISK**. Although doctors now explain our options, most people are not good at understanding risks and choosing sensibly. For example:

Women who have Nuchal Translucency screening for Down's Syndrome at 11-13 weeks are given the results in terms of a risk factor. In 2011 512 babies who had a definite diagnosis, not usually possible before 16 weeks, were aborted. In practice however, many women choose to abort at 11-13 weeks, citing another reason, because the abortion procedure is seen as less traumatic for both mother and foetus at that stage. A high risk factor might be less than 1 in 150 or 0.67% chance.

Baroness O'Neill also commented on the effect of **LEAGUE TABLES**, which reduce complex situations into statistics, on peoples' sense of responsibility. She suggested that the tables contribute to the common use of the **PRECAUTIONARY PRINCIPLE**, arguing that new treatments should be banned in case they cause any harm. She said that "there are also many demands for impractical levels of safety and success in medical practice", highlighting the role of politicians and the media in creating "a culture of blame and accusation" and in promoting uncritical thinking when it comes to discussing matters of life and death.

ANALYSING ARGUMENTS

Discussions about abortion, euthanasia, IVF or Genetic Engineering are often heated. It is important for students of ethics to see through the emotion and bluster and begin to analyse what is being said and evaluate the strengths and weaknesses of the different cases.

An argument is not abuse or straight contradiction, it is a point/ conclusion supported by one or more reasons/premises, for example: "I think abortion is wrong because human life is sacred". The presence of words such as because, therefore, so, thus or hence suggest that somebody is putting forward an argument.

Arguments can be good or bad. It depends on the number and/or strength of the reasons given and their relevance in supporting the point made with them. Points made without supporting reasons or citing irrelevant facts in support are obviously pretty worthless.

When developing arguments people often employ faulty reasoning, saying that such and such is true because of this and that - when this and that do not necessarily support it. Common faults in reasoning are called **FALLACIES** - here are a few which might appear in discussions about abortion, euthanasia, IVF or genetic engineering.

1. **CIRCULAR ARGUMENTS** are arguments that assume what they're trying to prove. If the conclusion of an argument is also one of its reasons, then the argument is circular, for example: "The murder of unborn children is wrong!".

2. An argument is **INCONSISTENT** if makes two or more contradictory claims. "I care about people and would do anything to stop innocent suffering! How can I stand by and allow labs to experiment on embryos?"

3. Some arguments **CONFUSE NECESSARY AND SUFFICIENT CONDITIONS**. "Human beings are unique in being rational; it is this which gives them moral status"- are all human beings rational or even potentially rational? Could rationality be a sufficient condition of personhood, but not a necessary condition?

4. Arguments that exclude some of the possible options from the outset commit the **RESTRICTING THE OPTIONS** fallacy. For example: "Either allow embryo research or don't - it is a straight choice!"

5. The **CORRELATION NOT CAUSATION** fallacy (sometimes called "post hoc", hasty generalisation or false cause) is committed when one reasons that just because two things are found together (i.e. are correlated) there must be a direct causal connection between them. For example: "The baby that was born after IVF and PGD had a genetic condition - the treatment must have caused it."

6. Arguments often use **SPECIFIC CASES TO SUPPORT GENERAL CONCLUSIONS**. For example: "People don't need

doctors to help them to die. My gran made up her mind that she had had enough and within a day she had gone naturally".

Journalists and politicians (and some members of RS classes) also use **RHETORICAL TECHNIQUES** to persuade people, which often conceal fallacies. Watch out for:

1. **STRAW MAN** arguments which misrepresent a position in order to attack it more easily, for example: "That's typical. Catholics say no to everything. You can't take them seriously because they just don't recognise the complexity of situations."

2. Discussions often involve claims about a **SLIPPERY SLOPE** , for example, that allowing Assisted Suicide for the terminally ill who request it will inevitably lead to all old people being compulsorily killed at 80.

3. Some discussions descend to a personal level quite quickly, for example: "you would be in favour of abortion on demand, given your behaviour on Saturday nights". Irrelevant personal comments are called **AD HOMINEM** attacks.

4. Sometimes people **APPEAL TO POPULARITY**, arguing that because lots of people believe something it must be true. For example: "We all believe that human life begins at conception, that there is something special about even the earliest stage embryo, don't we."

5. Sometimes discussions involve **APPEALS TO HISTORY**. People say "It has always been that way", or "it has always been done that way before" . For example: "This is a Catholic country. We have never tolerated suicide, even in cases of terminal illness, so we shouldn't start now!"

Finally, people often appeal to authorities to establish the reliability of facts or statistics. Sometimes the authorities cited do not have relevant or sufficient expertise or are not neutral, having a vested interest in what they say. However, whether they do or don't an **APPEAL TO AUTHORITY** will always be fallacious, because no matter how well-respected someone is, the fact that someone says that something is true doesn't in itself prove that it is true. For example: "my consultant says that IVF carries no more risk of producing a baby with a genetic problem."

KEY TERMS

ad hominem - beneficence - fallacy - non-maleficence - autonomy - Hippocratic Oath - informed consent - precautionary principle - slippery slope - straw man

SELF-ASSESSMENT QUESTIONS

1. What might inform a doctor's sense of what is ethical?

2. Explain the difference between a beneficence model of ethics and an autonomy model.

3. Think of three different situations in which doctors might find it difficult to preserve confidentiality.

4. Think of two cases in which confusion over who is the doctor's patient might affect decision-making.

5. Should a doctor ever take part in procedures against their conscience? Give examples to support your answer and consider most carefully what the conscience might be.

6. Review the Hippocratic Oath; how should the oath to be updated for today's Britain. Write your own version of the oath and then explain your reasoning.

7. Give an example of how people's perception of risk is not always accurate and how it might lead them to make irrational decisions.

8. Why might a shift from beneficence to autonomy in medical

ethics have led to a reduction in trust between doctors and patients?

9. Find an opinion-article relating to a medical issue. Respond to the argument in writing considering whether the author relies on fallacies or rhetorical devices and whether their point is properly supported.

10. To what extent do you agree with Baroness O'Neill that politicians and the media are partly to blame for creating a culture of blame and promoting uncritical thinking in medical issues?

FURTHER READING

- **O'NEILL, O.** - Autonomy and Trust in Bioethics, CUP 2002

- **HOPE, T.** - Medical Ethics: A Very Short Introduction, OUP 2004

- **BEAUCHAMP & CHILDRESS** - Principles of Biomedical Ethics, OUP 2008

- **HERREID & SCHILLER** - Science Stories, Science Teachers Association 2012

- **MCGEE, G.** - Bioethics for Beginners, Wiley 2012

Abortion

Abortion is the premature termination of a pregnancy, leading to the death of the embryo or foetus. This can be accidental in what is usually called a miscarriage or intentional in what is called a procured abortion or termination.

A large proportion of conceptions fail to produce a live birth. According to the Royal College of Obstetricians and Gynaecologists, following a positive pregnancy test women have about a 20% chance of early miscarriage. Many women miscarry before they are even aware that they are pregnant and, because of the risk, most delay talking about their pregnancy until the second trimester (weeks 13 to 28).

Procured abortions can be conducted in different ways:

- **ABORTOFACIENT** (causing abortion) emergency contraception (Levonelle or EllaOne "morning-after" pills and the emergency intrauterine device or **IUD**) works by causing any early-stage embryo not to implant. Progesterone only pills and devices and the IUD might also work in this way.

- Mifepristone, sometimes called RU486 or Mifegyne can be given to women in the first 9 weeks of pregnancy, causing a miscarriage. **MEDICAL ABORTIONS** are usually completed by administering a prostaglandin such as Misoprostol to stimulate uterine contractions.

- **SURGICAL ABORTIONS** up to 12 weeks are usually performed by vacuum aspiration, taking about 5 minutes. Between 13 and 19 weeks the cervix is opened manually and the contents of the uterus removed (Dilation and Curretage - **D&C**). Between 19 and 24 weeks (and later) drugs are given to prepare the cervix before the amniotic sac is injected with saline to kill the foetus and it is removed from the uterus, usually while the mother is under general anaesthetic.

- **PARTIAL BIRTH ABORTIONS** involve a doctor or midwife causing the death of the foetus before it draws its first breath.

STAGES OF DEVELOPMENT

Fertilisation	Sperm and egg fuse to form a single cell called a **ZYGOTE**
24-36 hours later	The single cell divides into two cells, then 12 hours later into 4 cells, then 12 hours later into 16 cells ...
3-4 days later	The zygote forms a cluster of cells called a **MORULA**. It enters the uterus
4 weeks pregnant *(about 4mm in size)*	The inner group of cells is now called an EMBRYO. Cells start to differentiate
5 weeks pregnant *(about 7mm in size)*	Neural tube forms. Blood circulation begins & heart starts to develop. Woman 'misses' her period
6-7 weeks pregnant *(about 8-10mm in size)*	The brain is developing distinct area. The heart begins to beat. 'Limb buds' show where the arms and legs are growing
8-9 weeks pregnant *(about 22mm in size)*	The baby is now called a FOETUS meaning 'young one'
10-12 weeks pregnant *(about 85mm in size)*	The foetus is now fully formed and moving about. Women are offered ultrasound scans to date the pregnancy and test for Down's Syndrome
13-20 weeks pregnant *(about 15cm in size)*	The baby is now growing quickly. The face begins to look much more human and the hair is beginning to grow as well as eyebrows and eyelashes
16-20 weeks pregnant	It may be possible to feel the baby moving from about 16 weeks **QUICKENING**. Diagnostic testing for Down's Syndrome is sometimes carried out
21-24 weeks pregnant *(about 27cm in size)*	From 20-21 weeks most doctors agree that the foetus responds to painful stimuli. 24 weeks is the upper limit for most abortions in the UK though 91% occur before 13 weeks
25-26 weeks pregnant *(about 29cm in size)*	The baby responds to touch and sound. The baby may also begin to follow a pattern for waking and sleeping
37-42 weeks pregnant	Birth. Most babies are born around the 40th week

THE LAW

In England, Wales and Scotland abortion was made legal in 1967, with the Abortion Act coming into effect in 1968. In 1990 the Human Fertilisation and Embryology Act modified the conditions under which abortion is legal, in particular lowering the upper time-limit for most procedures from 28 to 24 weeks. The law now reads:

Medical termination of pregnancy.

(1) Subject to the provisions of this section, a person shall not be guilty of an offence under the law relating to abortion when a pregnancy is terminated by a registered medical practitioner if two registered medical practitioners are of the opinion, formed in good faith—

(a) that the pregnancy has not exceeded its twenty-fourth week and that the continuance of the pregnancy would involve risk, greater than if the pregnancy were terminated, of injury to the physical or mental health of the pregnant woman or any existing children of her family; or

(b) that the termination is necessary to prevent grave permanent injury to the physical or mental health of the pregnant woman; or

(c) that the continuance of the pregnancy would involve risk to the life of the pregnant woman, greater than if the pregnancy

were terminated; or

(d) that there is a substantial risk that if the child were born it would suffer from such physical or mental abnormalities as to be seriously handicapped

According to the Department of Health:

- 189,931 abortions were carried out in England and Wales in 2011, the last year for which figures are available, 7.7% more than in 2001.

- 17.5 per 1,000 resident women aged 15-44 had abortions, double the 8.0 per 1,000 rate in 1970.

- 91% of 2011 abortions took place before 13 weeks.

- 47% of 2011 abortions were medical, 53% were surgical.

The Royal College of Obstetricians and Gynaecologists suggest that around 1 in 3 UK women have an abortion during their fertile lives. 7.6 million legal abortions have been carried out since 1968.

The law in Northern Ireland is less clear; as in the Republic of Ireland, the relevant law is still sections 58 and 59 of the Offences against the Person Act 1861, which makes it illegal to use drugs or instruments to procure abortion, and to supply or procure poison or instruments for the purpose of criminal abortion.

On 21st October 2012 Savita Halappanavar presented at University College Hospital in Galway, Republic of Ireland. She was miscarrying her 17 week pregnancy, but the foetus was still showing signs of life.

Doctors refused her request for an abortion, stating that "this is a Catholic country" despite the existence of a precedent which allowed abortion where "a pregnant woman's life was at risk because of pregnancy, including the risk of suicide". By the time the foetus died and the remains were removed from Ms. Halappanavar's uterus she had contracted septicaemia; she died on 28th October.

This case forced the Irish government to reconsider the country's position on abortion in extreme situations where womens' lives are in danger. It has also led to calls for the law in Northern Ireland to be clarified.

The law in both parts of Ireland reflects the fact that there is a majority of Roman Catholics.

RELIGIOUS TEACHING ON ABORTION

"Since the first century the Church has affirmed the moral evil of every procured abortion. This teaching has not changed and remains unchangeable." (Catechism 2271)

Whilst the Catechism suggests that the Christian position on Abortion is quite simple, in fact the debate about the moral status of unborn children and of early abortion has been live throughout the history of the Church.

Although no Christian has seen terminating a pregnancy as a good thing, or to be tolerated as a method of contraception, family planning or dealing with the consequences of rape, adultery or prostitution, relatively few Catholics saw early abortion as actual murder before the mid-nineteenth century.

Following St Augustine and St Thomas Aquinas, most scholars accepted that ensoulment did not take place at conception, but occurred later in pregnancy, perhaps at the point of quickening. It followed that early-stage abortions to save the life (or health) of a woman might be acceptable, if the procedure was less risky than continuing the pregnancy, which was rarely the case in the past.

In 1827 the human ovum was discovered and Aristotle's understanding of the origins of human life was finally laid to rest. Male and female were shown to share equally in creating a new life, which began a continuous process of development at the moment of conception. Afterwards few Christian scholars questioned the moral status of the unborn Child, though some still argued that abortion might be morally permissible in extreme circumstances.

From the 1860s, the Catholic Church seemed to become more and more conservative. Successive Popes ruled against those within the Church, mostly Jesuits, who had argued that the principle of double effect might permit some abortions even though the foetus is a person.

- Craniotomy, which cut up the head of a foetus stuck in the birth-canal, was banned in 1884 and again in 1889, even though it might save the life of a mother.

- In 1895 the Church taught that inducing birth prematurely in cases where the foetus was not viable was wrong.

- In 1889 it clarified that any direct killing of either foetus or mother to save one of the two is wrong.

- In 1902 it permitted removal of a fallopian tube, but ruled out the direct removal of an ectopic embryo (one growing outside the womb)- something which is controversial today as doctors can now laser the embryo, saving the tube.

- In 1930 Pope Pius XI again ruled out "the direct murder of the innocent", even as a means of saving the mother.

- In 1965 The Second Vatican Council declared: "Life must be protected with the utmost care from the moment of conception: abortion and infanticide are abominable crimes."

- In 1974 the Declaration on Procured Abortion stated that "The tradition of the Church has always held that human life must be protected and favoured from the beginning ... Opposing the morals of the Greco-Roman world, the Church of the first centuries insisted on the difference that exists on this point."

- In 1992 the Catechism stated that "The fifth commandment forbids ... direct abortion, willed as an end or as means, as well as cooperation in it." (Catechism 470). "Human life must be respected and protected absolutely from the moment of conception." (Catechism 2270)

- In 1995 Pope John Paul II wrote to women who had had an abortion "The Church is aware of the many factors which may have influenced your decision, and she does not doubt that... The wound in your heart may not yet have healed. Certainly what happened was and remains terribly wrong. But do not give in to discouragement." (Evangelium Vitae, 99)

So, although it was not until 1917 that the Catholic Church conclusively abandoned the distinction between early and later stage abortions, teaching had turned against any form of abortion, even if that meant allowing the deaths of both mother and child, well before this date.

Protestant Churches started the nineteenth century in a similar place to the Catholic Church but some chose to retain the idea that personhood is acquired gradually and depends on interests, capabilities and/or appearance as well as on brute DNA or any nebulous point of ensoulment. Today Anglican and Methodist churches teach that abortion is the lesser of two evils in cases where the real health or life of the mother is at risk. Although it is not desirable, when it comes about as a side-effect of treatment intended to benefit a woman then it is tolerated.

Conservative Protestant Churches (for example, Baptists) and Evangelicals take a harder line, tending to look to scripture for relevant guidance and settling on passages about the sanctity of life.

Within the Jewish tradition Exodus 21 says that if a pregnant woman is killed then, "a nefesh (human life) shall be given for a nefesh." however, if the woman miscarries but does not die, the killer must pay monetary damages. The implication is that the foetus is not a nefesh, a human life. The Mishnah teaches that:

"If a woman is undergoing a perilous pregnancy, the foetus may be destroyed since her life takes precedence over its life."

Moses Maimonides (d.1204) taught that aborting the foetus is permissible because it may be considered a rodef, one who "pursues" another with the intent to kill. When the foetus threatens the life of the pregnant woman, it is permissible or even obligatory to abort it. Within the Jewish tradition therefore, the therapeutic act of abortion might be seen as the moral equivalent to killing in self-defence.

While neither the Qur'an nor the Bible has any specific teaching on the moral status of the unborn, the Qur'an makes it clear that Allah decides that some pregnancies will not produce a live baby:

"We created you from dust, then from a sperm-drop, then from a clinging clot, and then from a lump of flesh, formed and unformed - that We may show you. And We settle in the wombs whom We will for a specified term." Qur'an 22:5

Nevertheless, it seems clear that it is not acceptable for human beings to interfere in the natural progress of having children.

"Do not kill your children out of poverty; We will provide for you and them…. And do not kill the soul which Allah has forbidden [to be killed] except by [legal] right." Qur'an 6:151 (see also Surah 17, verse 31)

Islamic scholars, like Christian scholars, sought to explain the point at which the unborn child became a person in terms of "ensoulment". Like Christian scholars, Islamic theologians were influenced by Aristotle and by the difficulty of establishing the gender of an embryo in stating that "ensoulment" took place anywhere between 30 and 120 days into pregnancy. Also like Christian scholars, some Islamic teachers permitted and permit early abortion on therapeutic grounds, when the procedure is less risky than the alternative and when it will save the life or health of a mother.

ABORTION AND RIGHTS

Today, discussions about abortion are closely bound up in discussions about human rights. To deny women control over their own bodies is seen by many feminist writers as an abuse of their **BASIC RIGHTS TO LIFE, LIBERTY AND SELF-DETERMINATION**. On the other hand, if the embryo/foetus is seen to be a person and to have rights of its own, nothing short of a straight choice between its life and that of its mother could hope to justify abortion.

It comes down to how rights are conceived of and what they depend on. Traditionally, rights were either seen as a **GIFT FROM GOD** (hence the human right to life is the equivalent of a belief in the Sanctity of Human Life) or as the manifestation of a **NATURAL LAW** (such as the natural law that human beings should live translates into a natural right to human life). During the enlightenment and into the 19th Century rights began to be seen as **THE RESULT OF BIOLOGICAL OR SOCIOLOGICAL DEVELOPMENT**; human beings realise that they need ground rules to govern all human interaction based on the principle of "do as you would be done to". Hume and later Weber saw rights in this way. Hobbes and later Rawls see rights as part of a **SOCIAL CONTRACT**; people surrender autonomy and money in return for protection from government or monarch and human rights codify some of the specific protections people expect.

Contemporary discussions are dominated by the **INTEREST THEORY** and the **WILL THEORY** of human rights.

- Interest theory bases human rights on human interests, the things which human beings want to do, for example, live, be healthy and happy.

- Will theory bases human rights on the human capacity for freedom, meaning nobody has the right to interfere with and constrain another person from doing what they want, except where their actions constrain others.

In both of these cases the human beings who have rights do so because they have interests and can be free, however it is not clear that an embryo, or even a foetus, would be covered. In cases where embryos exist in the lab with no willing mother and in cases where the foetus is sick, disabled or otherwise non-viable the idea that its rights should be considered as equal with the mother seems odd.

Nevertheless, it is difficult to prove that the unborn child has no rights. One of the most influential discussions of the issue in modern times makes no such assumption. For **JUDITH JARVIS THOMPSON**, the foetus might well have full human rights - but that does not necessarily rule out the mother's right to an abortion.

In a 1971 article Thompson used a thought-experiment to make her point.

A DEFENCE OF ABORTION

Imagine you wake up in hospital and are told that you have been involved in a car accident. The nurse explains that while you were in surgery a world-famous violinist was rushed into the same hospital. His friends urged the surgeon to help save his life by performing a new operation, whereby his blood-supply was hooked up to your vital organs, enabling his own heart, lungs, liver and kidneys to recover from trauma. You are a living life support system and will have to continue like this, in intensive care, for nine months pending a painful and slightly risky operation to separate you.

Do you have a moral obligation to stay in the intensive care unit sustaining the violinist's life?

For many people, the issue here is one of consent. If you agreed to sustain the violinist it seems like there would be more of an obligation than if you did or could not. The analogy seems to be with a woman pregnant by rape, though arguably it might also serve for any woman who used contraception and/or did not explicitly wish to become pregnant. Also, if the process of sustaining the violinist came to endanger your life or long term physical or mental health one might argue that the obligation grows less, even if you did consent.

Obviously, Thomson's argument has met with opposition.

From the perspective of Natural Law John Finnis takes issue with just about every point Thomson makes in "Abortion: A Reply to Judith Jarvis Thomson" (1973). For Finnis the foetus has a natural right to life equal to that of the mother and any direct action which causes its death is homicidal, regardless of the mother's intentions. No woman is ignorant of the effect of a termination on their unborn child so there is no way that the principle of double effect can legitimately be employed.

The feminist Mary-Anne Warren wrote that although Thomson's analogy is:

"Initially quite plausible in the normal case of an unwanted pregnancy we cannot claim that the woman is in no way responsible she could have remained chaste, or taken her pills more faithfully, or abstained on dangerous days if x behaves in a way (involving), say, a 1% chance of bringing into existence a human being with a right to life then it is by no means clear that x is free of any obligation to keep that human being alive".
(1973)

> *"My own intuition is that x has no more right to bring into existence, either deliberately or as a foreseeable result of action he could have avoided, a being with full moral rights (y) and then refuse to do what he knew beforehand would be required to keep that being alive ".*

In Practical Ethics (1982:132-4), Peter Singer responded to Thomson, concluding that her argument stands and falls by her theory of rights. Singer points out that Utilitarians would dismiss Thomson's contention that rights can be independent of what produces the greatest general happiness - elsewhere she suggests that a famous singer has the right to refuse to attend a sick fan, even if their doing so would cause a lot of happiness and could lead to the fan's recovery. He concludes that in cases where unplugging the violinist would cause more general misery than keeping him plugged in you have no right to unplug him - although that does not mean that Utilitarians would harangue or blame you for doing so.

The Virtue Ethicist Rosalind Hursthouse dismisses Thomson's argument, though she agrees that the operative issue is not whether the foetus has rights, (1991:223-246). She argues that the long-term effects of abortion on the mother and other interested parties, and on their future decision-making abilities, should be central to the discussion. The particular circumstances and motivations are totally relevant, as they make the difference between abortion leading to people flourishing and abortion leading to a cycle of misery. What is right for an eight year old abuse victim may not be right for a professional woman.

APPLYING ETHICAL THEORIES

Utilitarianism

For weak rule utilitarians such as John Stuart Mill, early-stage abortions which affect the mother alone are a matter for her alone to decide; the embryo/foetus cannot feel pain, let alone suffer and because the father and others do not know. In practice, there are few genuine act utilitarians today because most people accept that making fresh situational decisions is impractical if not impossible. Up to an agreed point in pregnancy, if termination will increase the woman's happiness then it would be right. Later-stage abortions are more complex, as the foetus has a clear ability to feel pain and definite potential to become a full human person. Other people will know about the abortion and will be concerned about it.

Stronger-rule utilitarians consider the general effects of allowing abortions in a range of generic situations. Allowing abortion-on-demand to the point of birth might produce more pain than pleasure to society in general, whereas allowing abortions in cases of rape, abuse or teenaged pregnancy would probably produce more pleasure. Famously RM Hare wrote an essay entitled "Could Kant have been a Utilitarian?", which implies that strong-rule utilitarianism could even yield the same sort of general, absolute prohibition on abortion as Kantian ethics might.

Kantian and Virtue ethics

Kant did not deal directly with the question of abortion or with when an unborn child might become a person. His **PRINCIPLE OF UNIVERSALIZATION** might suggest that abortion to save the health or life of the mother is alright - but at the risk of **OVER-PARTICULARIZING THE MAXIM**. Essentially, for Kant, the maxim of an action is what it is when all situational issues have been stripped away. If the embryo/foetus is a person then there is no getting away from the fact that the maxim of abortion is murder, which cannot be universalised in good conscience.

Kant's **PRACTICAL IMPERATIVE** demands that we treat all people as ends in themselves, never as means to an end. If the embryo/foetus is a person then abortion, even to save the life of the mother, could not be permitted. Kant's **PRINCIPLE OF A KINGDOM OF ENDS** demands that people consider the precedent that their actions set for others. Permitting abortions, even for compelling reasons, might contribute to what the Roman Catholics have called a "culture of death", setting a poor example for other people in terms of care of the vulnerable and respect for humanity.

So, is the embryo/foetus a person for Kant? His answer is quite difficult. We cannot know whether it is or it isn't but it is reasonable to treat everything human as if it might be. It seems probable that Kant would have afforded the embryo/foetus respect and dignity and that he would have interpreted the **CATEGORICAL IMPERATIVE** to mean that abortion should not be accepted.

What have modern Kantians said about this issue? Christine Korsgaard considers whether the unborn child deserves respect. She writes

"Kant grounds morality in a feature of human subjectivity. That is the form of self-consciousness that, as I said earlier, makes us capable of assessing the grounds of our beliefs and actions, determining whether those grounds count as good grounds or not, and issuing laws to ourselves accordingly. This form of self-consciousness ... does not apply to the other animals." (Valuing Our Humanity)

Nevertheless, she suggests that even if a non-moral being has no moral value as such, that does not make disregarding its interests acceptable, concluding

"Valuing our humanity, I conclude, involves a number of different things. It involves … respecting the rational choices of other people, and making ourselves fit to make rational choices... And it also involves, quite simply, caring about ourselves and each other … it does not involve considering ourselves superior to other living beings, or require us to limit our moral concern to human beings alone. In fact perhaps there is no better way of expressing the value we set on our humanity, than by extending the reach of our moral concern beyond the boundaries of humanity itself." (Valuing Our Humanity)

Both RM Hare and Harry Gensler start from the Kantian Principle of Universalization. RM Hare stated that 'abortion [is] prima facie and in general wrong', (1989:29) and Harry Gensler agreed, suggesting that "abortion is wrong and that certain Kantian consistency requirements more or less force us into thinking this', (1986:83). He observed that most of us would be glad that our mothers did not abort us, so we should see that abortion is generally undesirable and should not be permitted in "special" circumstances without very careful thought as to the general consequences of doing so.

Nevertheless, Susan Feldman and Lara Denis have come to different conclusions, arguing that Kantian principles point towards abortion being morally problematic, but not always wrong.

Feldman questions Gensler's argument, arguing that it is possible **BOTH** to be glad to be alive **AND** to accept that one's mother had the right to abort. Feldman sees a maxim as the subjective principle of action, including reasons and desires, so she has little difficulty in distinguishing between situations in which abortion is universally permissible and situations in which it would not be. For Feldman, Kantian ethics is little more than weak-rule-utilitarianism. Taking the particular situation, replete with the details of mitigating circumstances, motivations and intentions, we should just reflect on whether we could accept other people doing the same as we propose to do.

Denis interprets Kant in terms of Virtue Ethics. For Kant there are two types of duty. **PERFECT** duties are (normally) absolute prohibitions, for example, do not murder, do not lie, do not steal. **IMPERFECT** duties are (normally) positive, for example, help others in need, develop one's talents. Kant argues that perfect duties never conflict and where a perfect duty conflicts with an imperfect duty, the perfect duty must prevail. In other words, a negative always trumps a positive for Kant.

Denis focuses on the perfect duties which virtuous people have towards themselves, such as not to do anything to physically or emotionally harm ourselves, when doing so will impact on our ability to function rationally and be good. When pregnancy threatens life, or physical or mental health, Denis seems to reason, it could be a duty to terminate it.

Furthermore, while reason should be in control, pregnancy causes emotion and/or instinct to take over sometimes, making pregnant women vulnerable to making irrationally altruistic or selfish or short-sighted decisions. They must guard against this and ensure that all decisions are led by reason. This might be a reason for a Kantian woman choosing not to become pregnant in the first place, if not for aborting early-on.

Although Denis asserts that the foetus does not deserve full moral status, she accepts that it is a perfect duty to preserve useful emotions. Most women feel attached to their unborn children and are upset at the thought of harming them; it is rational to preserve these feelings, so aborting is morally problematic, if not absolutely wrong.

As McCoy points out, Denis is rather vague over what might make an abortion right, but surely this is typical of a Virtue approach to applied ethics (2011). It is not possible to prescribe a course of action for another person; the role of the philosopher is just to suggest lines of reasoning which will be helpful in guiding peoples thought processes in deciding for themselves.

This is consistent with Kant's own approach, despite the fact that he is more usually associated with lists of inflexible rules. For Kant a good will always acts freely and rationally - any action motivated by habit or obedience is actually evil, even if it appears to be good - so it is vital for Kant that people make decisions for themselves and that their autonomy is not eroded by over-zealous "advice".

The practical implication of a Virtue approach to abortion is that abortion should be available "on demand" at least for the first part of pregnancy, and that thorough counselling services should be made available both to women considering termination and following termination.

Natural Law

Most moral philosophers of the natural law tradition also operate within a religious world-view, accepting that human life is sacred, probably from conception. For John Finnis a modern Roman Catholic philosopher, abortion is equivalent to murder and absolutely wrong because it removes the embryo/foetus ability to live or fulfil any of the **BASIC GOODS** of humanity (1973:117-145).

PROPORTIONALISTS such as Bernard Hoose would suggest that direct abortion might, in some cases, be **THE LESSER OF TWO EVILS** or be justified through the **PRINCIPLE OF DOUBLE EFFECT**. For examples, in the case of an eight year old victim of gang-rape in war or in the case of a woman with an ectopic pregnancy.

However Germain Grisez would disagree with this approach, arguing abortion would simply compound the sin of the rapists, making the victim into a murderess rather than supporting her in her plight and that the principle of double effect cannot justify consequences which are fully known to be the inevitable result of an action.

Situation Ethics

Situationism has, of course, been rejected by mainstream churches because of the responsibility it places on individuals to make decisions based on agape and the particular circumstances, however it would be wrong to suggest that it would always accept abortion. As conceived of by William Temple and even by Joseph Fletcher Situation Ethics has to have regard for the values and laws of society and for the effects decisions might have on the wider community. Agape, properly understood, is **NON-PREFERENTIAL LOVE**. The interests of the father must be considered alongside the mother - and the foetus, if it is capable of having interests.

KEY TERMS

abortofacient - contraception - zygote - embryo - foetus - proportionalism - perfect duties - imperfect duties - universalization - means and ends - Will Theory of Rights, Interest Theory of Rights - viability - quickening

SELF-ASSESSMENT QUESTIONS

1. What is an Abortion?

2. What do Christians, Jews and Muslims teach about abortion? Why?

3. When does the Law permit an abortion in the UK?

4. Given the numbers of abortions in the UK, do you think there is a need for the law to change? How and why?

5. To what extent can an embryo have rights?

6. Do you find Judith Jarvis Thomson's thought experiment convincing? Explain your answer.

7. Is it fair to say that Utilitarians would always approve of abortion?

8. "Kantian Ethics is absolutely against abortion!" Do you agree?

Explain your answer with reference to the views of different Kantian scholars.

9. Describe and explain how one Virtue Ethicist has responded to the issue of Abortion.

10. Would Natural Law necessarily rule out allowing women with ectopic pregnancies to have terminations?

FURTHER READING

- **WILCOCKSON, M.** - Medical Ethics, Hodder 2008

- **GLOVER, J.** - Causing Death &Saving Lives, Penguin 1990

- **KACZOR, C.** - The Ethics of Abortion: Women's Rights, Human Life, and the Question of Justice, Routledge 2013

- **BROCKOPP, J.E.** (ed.) - Islamic Ethics of Life, University of South Carolina Press 2003

IVF and Fertility Treatment

The options open to couples struggling to have a baby have increased radically since the first IVF "test tube baby", Louise Brown, was born in 1978. Today, around 60,000 fertility treatments are administered in UK clinics each year, overseen by the Human Fertilisation and Embryology Authority (**HFEA**) which was set up by the 1990 Human Fertilisation and Embryology Act, which also lays down the legal principles governing these treatments.

In the last 30 years rates of infertility have increased substantially.

- According a 2012 study of 26,600 men in France, average male sperm-counts in Europe have declined, from 73.6 million/ml in 1989 to 49.9 million/ml in 2005. The proportion of normally formed sperm also decreased by 33.4 per cent over the same period. According to the World Health Organisation, concentrations less than 55 million/ml make it more difficult to conceive. It is thought that around 20% of young British men are now infertile, which is defined as having sperm counts lower than 15.5 million/ml.

- According to the OECD, the average age at which British women have their first baby increased to 30 in 2009, compared with 28 in Australia, 25 in the USA and 21 in Mexico. The risks for both mother and baby increase when women have babies after the age of 35, and female fertility rates fall from around the age of 27. According to an article in the journal Human Reproduction, by the time a woman reaches 35, her chances of getting pregnant during any particular attempt are about half of what they were between the ages of 19 and 26.

- Rates of diseases and other conditions affecting fertility, from testicular cancer to chlamydia, are on the increase.

- About 1 in 6 couples, or 3.5 million people in the UK, are affected by infertility at any one point.

- Increasingly, single people and same-sex couples are seeking to start a family using assisted reproduction.

This has increased the demand for fertility treatments, putting a strain on the NHS in the UK and putting another strain on peoples' finances, when they have to pay for private care.

TREATMENTS AVAILABLE

- Fertility drugs are often used to regulate the cycle and stimulate ovaries into producing more eggs. They can be used alone or as a prelude to IVF. Egg-donors are usually given fertility drugs prior to donating.

- Male fertility can sometimes be improved using drugs or hormones, or sperm can be extracted directly from the testicles.

- Eggs and sperm can be frozen prior to use. This is often done in the case of donor eggs or donor sperm, but increasingly it is being offered to people undergoing cancer-treatment which might affect fertility, and is even being offered by commercial egg-banks to young women who might donate some eggs, keeping others in storage for possible use later on. Indications are that freezing barely affects sperm, but causes eggs to be less likely to result in a live-birth.

- Artificial Insemination (**AI** or **IUI**) can be used to ensure that sperm is delivered to the right place at the right time; this is often when donor sperm is being used (AID or IUI Donor).

- In Vitro Fertilisation (**IVF**) involves mixing eggs and sperm, either or both could be from a donor, in a petri dish and collecting resulting embryos for re-implantation. Currently, most clinics re-implant 1-2 embryos per cycle. 60% of IVF cycles are funded privately in the UK and 80% of those using a donor. In 2011, the overall live-birth rate per cycle of IVF was 24.5%, up from 14% in 1991.

- Intra-cycloplasmic sperm injection (**ICSI**) is a technique whereby a single sperm is injected directly into an egg; it is sometimes used as part of IVF where it would otherwise be difficult to achieve any embryos.

- Various techniques are offered to help select the best embryos for implantation or to help those embryos implant successfully, including **EEVA** (early embryonic viability assessment) time-lapse imaging and assisted hatching, whereby the coating of the embryo is opened to help it to implant.

- IVF embryos can be screened using **PREIMPLANTATION GENETIC DIAGNOSIS** (**PGD**), which involves removing one or two cells and checking the genetic material. Desirable embryos can then be implanted in the normal way. PGD can be used to screen and select embryos on **THERAPEUTIC** grounds or in order to create a **SAVIOUR SIBLING**. It can also be used to select embryos on grounds of gender or other genetic traits, but this has been illegal in the UK since 2008.

- A **SURROGATE** mother can be used to carry a baby for a woman who is unable or unwilling to go through pregnancy; the surrogate is given AI or has IVF embryos created and implanted, either using the male partner's sperm or a donor's sperm. In some rare cases, a surrogate is implanted with an embryo created using donor eggs as well.

LEGAL ISSUES ARISING

Payment

Under the terms of the 1990 Act, donors and surrogates may not be paid; only expenses may be covered by recipients or clinics. This has led to a real shortage in donors, particularly of eggs. Egg-donation involves at least a month of being injected with strong drugs - it is a drawn-out, unpleasant and invasive procedure and not many women want to go through it for pure altruism.

Some schemes allow women to offset part of the cost of their own IVF if they agree to donate a fixed number of eggs to other women. Other schemes encourage young women to have a cycle of eggs harvested, to freeze some for their own possible use and to donate others as a means of offsetting the cost of treatment and storage.

Surrogacy

In the UK the surrogate mother remains the legal parent of the child until the recipient couple legally adopt it after the birth. In the UK, regardless of whether the child is biologically related to one or both recipient parents, they have no right to force the surrogate mother to give up her child or have medical procedures or abortions to which she does not consent. Within the UK it is more common for surrogacy to be within a family, say the sister or mother of an infertile woman, than to use an unrelated woman. Increasingly however, couples are using overseas surrogates in India or another country and then seeking to adopt and bring the child back to the UK.

In countries such as Australia, where **COMMERCIAL SURROGACY** is also illegal, overseas surrogacy is becoming popular amongst wealthy couples, homosexual couples and single career-women. There have been questions asked over whether the biological children of Australians should have automatic citizenship when they are born to overseas mothers overseas.

Welfare

Any fertility centre in the United Kingdom offering treatment must take account of the welfare of any children or potential children involved.

Clinics need to consider:

- Age and likely future ability to look after or provide for a child's need.

- Their commitment to having and bringing up a child, or children.

- Economic status, their ability to meet the needs of any child or children born as a result of treatment.

- Home environment and effect of new babies upon any existing children.

- Mental and physical health of the parents.

- The medical and family history of the couples and their families.

- Criminal history of parents.

- If they have any history of child-neglect or child-abuse.

- The potential for children needing to know about their origin.

The HFEA has ruled that women under the age of 40 should be limited to two embryos being implanted per cycle. Spare embryos may be frozen, but must be destroyed after 10 years. In 2008 the HFEA decided that PGD should only be used for therapeutic reasons, not for gender selection or aesthetic reasons.

The **ANONYMITY** of sperm and egg donors was abolished in 2005, meaning that any person born as a result of donation after 1st April 2005 is entitled to request and receive their donor's name and last known address, once they reach the age of 18. As a donor, you have no legal rights to contact your donor-conceived offspring; the decision to initiate contact is solely that of the donor-conceived child.

The law on **LEGAL PARENTHOOD** following fertility treatment changed in 2009. Since then, it has been possible for the partner in a same sex couple to be registered as the second parent to a child born from licensed fertility treatment.

In the UK demand for IVF and related fertility treatments has been increased by the inefficiencies of the **ADOPTION SYSTEM**, which can make it much more difficult for people to adopt a child than to go through the process of assisted conception. For whatever reason, clinics take a broader view of child welfare than do council adoption services.

AROUND THE WORLD

- In Germany the freezing of embryos banned; couples must produce fresh embryos for a second attempt with IVF.

- In France lesbians are not allowed access to donor sperm, while Egypt and Saudi Arabia ban all procedures which use donated sperm or eggs and surrogacy.

- In Norway, homosexuals can be accepted for infertility treatment but surrogacy is banned - meaning that lesbians can have their own biological offspring but gay couples cannot.

- In Italy a requirement that all embryos produced for IVF must be replaced in the womb was reversed in 2010, following a legal challenge that it was not best medical practice.

- In New Zealand the requirement to consider the welfare of the child no longer means it must be raised in a nuclear family. The Maori idea of the family includes the practice of guardianship.

- In South Africa surrogacy for non-residents is banned, though it is widespread in India and largely unregulated.

There are several different ethical issues raised by IVF and fertility treatments.

ETHICAL ISSUES

The "right to a child"

This complex area involves asking questions such as:

- Do people have a right to a child? How about when natural conception seems impossible?

- How far can and should a right be taken? Does it just suggest that people should be free from physical or legal interference and constraint - or does it confer an obligation on doctors or the state?

- Who should pay for (how much) IVF or other fertility treatment?

- Should the number or type of treatments be limited - on what grounds?

- Who is eligible for treatment? Should single people, same-sex couples, prisoners or women of 14 or 56 be treated?

- Who should decide who gets NHS treatment and how much? In the past, Local Heath Authorities taking on this responsibility has led to a **POSTCODE LOTTERY**.

- Do people have the right to choose the gender or other characteristics of their children, to decide exactly when and how they have children?

- Do parents have the right to use PGD to create a genetically-suitable "saviour sibling" or even to create a replacement for a dead child?

- Do all the available treatments respect the rights of all those concerned?

- Should egg, sperm or embryo donors, or surrogates, be paid? (Bear in mind that the number of people willing to donate or act as a surrogate without payment is very small and not paying could mean many people waiting for or never getting fertility treatment.)

- Should donors and surrogates have parental rights and responsibilities over the children born as a result of their donations? Should this include having to pay child support maintenance and should the parents of a surrogate baby be able to force a surrogate mother to abort a baby diagnosed with a disability at 12 weeks?

- Should donors and/or surrogates have a right to anonymity, even when that means children being unable to trace biological relations?

Central to questions about rights to a child is what a right really might be. Amartya Sen admits that "worries relate to what is taken to be the "softness" (some would say "mushiness") of the conceptual grounding of human rights", (2004:315). The real issue here is the "rights" that people appeal to as a basis for a change in the law or a change in the interpretation of the law, not the rights which have already been enshrined in law.

▶ Religious Teaching and Rights to a Child

Although Religious people see having children as part of God's plan for humanity, no Christian, Jewish or Muslim scholar would argue that there is any obligation to provide fertility treatment in cases where a couple are unable to have children naturally. Religious leaders will sympathise with the plight of childless couples and single people who have not found a suitable partner, but will rarely suggest that either IVF or surrogacy is the best way to deal with their feelings.

Pope Benedict XVI said:

"The Church pays great attention to the suffering of couples with infertility, she cares for them and, precisely because of this, encourages medical research". (Vatican Radio 25.02.12)

But he warned against the lure of Artificial Insemination and IVF, which is prohibited by the Church. This is because:

- A child has the right to be conceived naturally.

- Human sexuality is both unitive and procreative; IVF makes procreation the only goal of sex, which is as bad as using contraception, which makes uniting a couple its only goal. Pope Paul VI spoke of the "inseparable connection, willed by God, and unable to be broken by man on his own initiative, between the two meanings of the conjugal act: the unitive meaning and the procreative meaning."

- Building on Natural Law, the church sees human life as potentially beginning at conception and any destruction of embryos, even those which are non-viable, as wrong and as contributing to a "culture of death".

- IVF threatens to turn children into commodities and to erode the sanctity of life by unduly interfering in the mysterious process of creating new life.

In particular, many Christians will question whether it would be right for a child to be brought up by single people, prisoners or same-sex couples. The parents' rights should always be balanced against the rights and best interests of the child.

Adoption has long been promoted by Churches as matching a child's need with that of prospective parents. Catholic and Anglican adoption agencies still dominate this field in many countries, providing a real alternative to abortion and reducing the demand for expensive and difficult fertility treatments.

Muslim teaching has a particular difficulty with the use of donor sperm because the Qur'an teaches that placing sperm in a forbidden womb is the essence of adultery, a major sin. Shi'ite Muslims have, on occasion, got around this difficulty through arranging temporary divorces and temporary marriages between donors and recipients, but Sunni Muslim scholars teach that these are forbidden. Muslims do not see early-embryos as persons and rarely object to IVF when a husband's sperm and a wife's eggs are used, though they might be concerned about how much interference there is in the natural process of procreation, especially when extensive screening of the embryos is carried out for non-medical reasons. The Qur'an teaches:

"To God belongs the dominion of heavens and earth. He creates what He wills. He bestows female (offspring) upon whom He wills, and bestows male (offspring) upon whom He wills. Or He

bestows both males and females, and He leaves childless whom He wills." (Qur'an 42:49-50)

Nevertheless, children are seen as a blessing and to complete a couple's relationship, so any reasonable support which doctors can give to infertile couples is positive.

▸ Applying Ethical theories to the right to a child

Utilitarianism might support a limited number of IVF cycles being paid for by the NHS, providing that the cost did not become unmanageable and the benefits justified it. Similarly, Situation Ethics would speak in favour of couples being helped, whenever doing so did not threaten the wellbeing of other interested parties.

Virtue Ethics might take a longer view, warning of the possible consequences for individuals and society in general if children are seen as a right and somehow commoditised.

Kantian Ethics sees perfect duties, not to do something harmful, as taking priority over imperfect duties to do something beneficial. The duty to help infertile couples cannot, therefore, extend so far as to justify governments getting into debt. Kant would not have accepted that having children was anybody's right. He himself decided not to marry or enjoy a family because his wealth was insufficient to care for a wife and family properly - and his attentions were focused on work.

What Natural Law would say depends on the list of "basic goods" suggested. For Aquinas, having children is part of any fulfilled life and there is some sense of a right to a child, however life itself is primary, so any treatment which caused the death of embryos would not be permitted. However in 1980 John Finnis described the "basic goods" of human life in terms of life, knowledge, aesthetic appreciation, play, friendship, practical reasonableness, and religion, adding "the marital good" in 1996. In 1995 Timothy Chappell listed friendship, aesthetic value, pleasure and the avoidance of pain, physical and mental health and harmony, reason, rationality, and reasonableness, truth and the knowledge of it, the natural world, people, fairness, and achievements. Children are not an essential part of human goodness for either of these scholars, though they would be a welcome addition.

For Finnis, as for Aquinas, life is a basic good and this would stand in the way of using embryos as a means to an end of having children through IVF.

Saviour Siblings

In 2010 Megan Matthews received a bone-marrow transplant from her brother Max. It enabled her to overcome Fanconi Anaemia, a rare inherited condition which had caused bone-marrow failure, meaning that she could not produce blood and needed transfusions every couple of weeks.

Megan's case was special because Max was created specifically to become her ideal donor, after searches for another donor failed.

Using PGD to select embryos free from generic defects and compatible with an existing child has been allowed by the HFEA, but not without controversy. Following the Matthews case the Director of Comment on Reproductive Ethics said of Max:

> "He owes his life to his capacity to be of therapeutic use to his sick sister, otherwise he would not have been chosen in the first

place... this is the big ethical problem." (BBC News, 21.12.10)

Of course, Kate Matthews, Megan and Max's mother said:

"*Max is loved for being him and not for what he has done. He has completed our family and now I have a bubbly and healthy girl.*" (BBC News, 21.12.10)

But critics observe that parents would say that, whether or not their motivations and psychological relationship with the new child were really healthy.

In 2003 Charlie Whittaker was given a transplant of blood cells from a saviour sibling created for him in a US Fertility Clinic. The HFEA previously gave permission to the Hashmis to treat their sick son Zain, who was 4 years old. The HFEA stated that

"*We have to look at the benefit for the embryo, not just the sibling ... we have to be quite strict in the way we issue licences. We look at the scientific, medical and moral issues before making any decision. HFEA policy states women are allowed to have treatment only for the benefit of the embryo. It is a tough decision to make.*" (Daily Telegraph, 20.6.03)

Ethical concerns focus on the fate of the discarded embryos created in the process of IVF, whether deemed to have the genetic defect or not.

From a Natural Law perspective, these embryos are potential persons and should not be destroyed, regardless of the situation. Similarly, Kantian ethics would be concerned about anything that suggested that one person could or should be used as a means of securing the health or life of another.

Virtue Ethics would probably worry about the family relationships which might be affected by the creation of a saviour sibling and the long term consequences.

Utilitarian calculations would very much depend on the circumstances and how long-term and big-picture the calculations were allowed to be. The precedent of allowing children to be "designed" is potentially dangerous and if the law is not sufficiently specific then the ends might not outweigh the means.

The treatment of "spare embryos"

IVF and related treatment involve creating a large number of embryos, of which only a few are implanted into a woman. The rest are usually frozen and eventually destroyed, either actively or passively. The freezing process itself causes some embryos to be lost or become less viable, though new vitrification techniques are less harmful.

Some women choose to donate their spare embryos, either for use in other women who cannot conceive naturally or for research purposes.

In some cases, screening shows that the spare embryos are genetically defective or otherwise unlikely to be viable, but in others these embryos could result in live births, if there was a willing and able mother.

The treatment of "spare embryos" raises particular issues for those who believe that personhood might begin at conception and is not dependent on capabilities or interests. For Roman Catholics, the idea that any embryo is "spare" creates the sense that human life can be used as a means to an end. It contributes to a wider "culture of death" in which the vulnerable cease to be properly respected. No matter what benefits IVF or research might bring, it cannot be worth the destruction of human lives.

Selective abortion

This was more of an issue in the past than it is today, when IVF clinics implant multiple embryos and a multiple pregnancy results, women must choose whether to continue and accept the higher risks that come with having twins or triplets, or to terminate one or more of the foetuses, in order to give the remaining pregnancy the best chance.

Selective abortion carries with it all the moral problems of any abortion - but it also raises questions about whether and how embryos or foetuses can be selected for abortion, by whom, on what grounds and for what ends.

Informed Consent

Most clinics are obviously commercial enterprises, competing to make money. Most people seeking fertility treatments are desperate and may not be in a position to make a rational decision about complicated, expensive and invasive procedures. Ethical questions over the way in which information is made available to patients, over marketing strategies and over pricing are often raised.

For example, some clinics have started to promote "Natural IVF", charging couples as much or more for this treatment than for standard IVF - although it is cheaper to deliver and is less effective, at a success rate of 7% per cycle rather than 25%. Some marketing materials seem to suggest that the treatment "works in harmony with your body" with lots of pictures of happy families in the country, when in fact this is much the same treatment as standard IVF, without using fertility drugs to stimulate the production of multiple eggs beforehand. Yes, women experience fewer medicinal side-effects - but they might well have to pay for several sequences of invasive egg-harvesting and more cycles of IVF in the end - going through more stress before achieving a pregnancy.

For another example, clinics recently started offering couples a new form of embryo-screening called Eeva, which uses time-lapse photography to record the division of the cells and help doctors to choose the "best" embryos to implant. The scientific study which this treatment was based on was very small-scale and some experts have pointed out that there is no proof that the procedure made any difference. Yet that does not stop clinics from charging £800 per cycle without making the potential problems clear in the literature.

The HFEA can do little when clinics operate abroad.

There has been a sharp rise in couples choosing to have IVF abroad, such as in Spain or the Czech Republic where cycles start from about £2000 (compared with about £3500 in London) and where regulation is much lighter. Egg and sperm donors can often be paid well and guaranteed anonymity in other countries, making donor procedures more widely available. Four embryos are routinely implanted, whereas most clinics limit women under the age of forty to two in the UK.

Other couples choose to go to the USA, where prices are higher but where cutting edge techniques such as using prenatal diagnosis (PGD) for gender selection and even eye and hair colour are already available.

KEY TERMS

IVF - assisted reproduction - artificial insemination (IUI) - surrogate - Intra-cytoplasmic sperm injection (ICSI) - prenatal genetic diagnosis (PGD) - early embryo viability assessment test (Eeva) - saviour sibling - Human Embryo and Fertilisation Authority (HFEA)

SELF-ASSESSMENT QUESTIONS

1. What is IVF?

2. What regulations are there applying to fertility treatment in the UK?

3. To what extent do people have a "right to a child"?

4. "Natural Law sees having children as a basic good of humanity; therefore it supports infertile couples using IVF to start a family." Do you agree? Explain your answer.

5. Write a paragraph of 150 words explaining the Roman Catholic teaching on IVF.

6. How do Islamic teachings differ from Christian teachings? Why?

7. To what extent would Kantian Ethics support infertile couples receiving 3 cycles of IVF on the NHS?

8. Would Utilitarianism support the state treating the 3.5 million infertile people with whatever medical means necessary to assist conception?

9. Would there be a difference between the views of Bentham and Singer on this question?

10. Should the UK legalise PGD for gender selection? Explain your answer and explore how it relates to at least two other perspectives

FURTHER READING

- **WARNOCK, M.** - Making Babies: Is there a right to have children?, Oxford Paperbacks 2003

- **DEECH & SMAJDOR** - From IVF to Immortality: Controversy in the Era of Reproductive Technology, OUP 2007

- **GLOVER, J.** - Choosing Children: Genes, Disability, and Design, OUP 2008

- **GEORGE & TOLLEFSON** - Embryo: A Defense of Human Life (2nd Ed), The Witherspoon Institute (2011)

- **BLYTH & LANDAU** (Eds) - Faith and Fertility: Attitudes Towards Reproductive Practices in Different Religions from Ancient to Modern Times, Jessica Kingsley Publishers (2009)

Embryo Research

The creation of "spare embryos" through IVF has enabled scientists to study the development of the embryo, often with a view to improving fertility treatments but sometimes with a view to developing other medical treatments.

Most widespread is the research being carried out on **EMBRYONIC STEM-CELLS**.

In 1998 James Thomson, a scientist at the University of Wisconsin, successfully removed cells from spare embryos at fertility clinics and grew them in the laboratory. He launched the modern field of stem cell research and established the world's first **HUMAN EMBRYONIC STEM CELL LINE** which still exists today.

In the early stages of development an embryo consists of stem-cells, cells which have the potential to become any different type of cell.

Within an embryo, the earliest cells are known as **TOTIPOTENT** and can develop into a whole new organism.

Later, cells become **PLURIPOTENT** and can develop into 200 different types of cell, given the correct stimulus.

Embryonic pluripotent stem-cells offer the potential of new treatments for spinal injuries, loss of sight or degenerative illnesses such as Parkinson's disease, though none of these embryonic treatments is yet available.

The first human trial for spinal injury victims was approved by the US

Food and Drug Administration (**FDA**) in 2009, however in 2011 the company announced that it will discontinue further development of its stem cell programs, perhaps partially because of the intense controversy and media attention which it attracted.

Obviously, harvesting the stem-cells from embryos causes the destruction of that embryo, although as a "spare" created in an IVF lab it never had the potential to develop, let alone lead to a live birth.

Ethical concerns have been raised about using embryos for research and for therapeutic treatments

1. Essentially, both research and treatments use embryos as **A MEANS TO AN END** of improving knowledge, treating disease or disability or even saving life.

2. For those who believe that human life should be treated as **SACRED FROM CONCEPTION**, all forms of embryo research, including embryonic stem cell research, are wrong regardless of the hope they might offer to other people.

3. Other people are concerned that embryonic stem-cell research **SETS A PRECEDENT** that human life is somehow expendable, and might be the beginning of a **SLIPPERY SLOPE** towards a society where the vulnerable can be destroyed if the benefits to the strong are clear. This has been referred to in terms of a **CULTURE OF DEATH**.

4. There are concerns that treatments will be **VERY COSTLY** and only available to the rich; they could push health-insurance premiums out of the reach of ordinary people and break national health systems like the NHS.

5. There are also concerns about the **LONG-TERM SAFETY** of treatments which involve introducing cells directly into, say the brain - though people such as the actor Michael J Fox, who suffers from Parkinson's Disease, point out that these treatments are a last resort and any side-effects are insignificant in comparison with the certain death some conditions promise otherwise.

Famously, President George W. Bush, an Evangelical Christian, removed federal funding from labs working on new human embryonic stem-cell lines in 2000, meaning that research on embryonic stem-cells is now conducted by major universities, usually in conjunction with drug-companies. Showing that such political moves do not prevent scientific advances from being made, in May 2013, scientists from Oregon announced that they had successfully **CLONED HUMAN EMBRYOS** to the 5 day, 150-cell "blastocyst" stage - when they could be used to harvest embryonic stem-cells. This could get around the main problem with embryonic stem-cell research and treatments, that donated eggs and embryos are in short-supply.

Dr Shoukhrat Mitalipov said:

"A thorough examination of the stem cells derived through this technique demonstrated their ability to convert just like normal embryonic stem cells, into several different cell types, including nerve cells, liver cells and heart cells… While there is much work to be done in developing safe and effective stem cell treatments, we believe this is a significant step forward in developing the cells that could be used in regenerative medicine." (BBC News, 15.5.13)

The creation of cloned human embryos, even if just for research purposes, remains highly controversial, both with religious groups and with others who have concerns about the safety and future uses of this research.

THE LAW

Embryo research

In the UK HFEA licensed labs can harvest and experiment on embryos up until 14 DAYS of development. This point was deemed significant by Baroness Warnock and her committee, on whose report the 1990 Act was based, because after this stage an embryo cannot split into twins. Germ-line genetic engineering, which includes any actual changes to the genetic makeup of the embryo which is then implanted, is not allowed in the UK.

Hybrids

In May 2008 a cross-party attempt to ban **HYBRID HUMAN-ANIMAL EMBRYOS** was defeated on a free vote in the House of Commons, by 336 to 176. MPs had been debating the Human Fertilisation and Embryology Bill, which would allow regulated research using hybrid or 'admix' embryos, where the nuclei of human cells are inserted into animal eggs.

Currently, **CYTOPLASMIC EMBRYOS** are most commonly created by transferring nuclei from human cells into the sacs of animal eggs. The resulting embryos are 99%+ human. These embryos are grown for less than 14 days before being harvested for stem cells, for use in research. The technique is popular because there is a shortage of human eggs in the UK, because women are not allowed to be paid to donate. UK scientists do not intend to create human-animal-hybrid **CHIMERAS**.

Christian groups worry that such procedures fail to respect the sanctity of life. Muslim groups are opposed as both the Qur'an and scholarship teaches that the line between species must never be crossed.

ADULT STEM CELLS

A different type of stem cell is also found in adults, within bone-marrow, fat or blood or from amniotic-fluid or cord-blood. Adult Stem Cells are rarely pluripotent; more usually they are **MULTIPOTENT**, being able to develop into a number of different types of cell within a close family group. Treatments based on these adult stem-cells are currently being trialled and used around the world for leukaemia and some types of heart disease.

INDUCED PLURIPOTENT STEM CELLS (IPS CELLS)

In 2007 Dr Shinya Yamanaka and Dr John Gurdon were awarded the Nobel Prize for Medicine in 2012. They discovered how to re-program adult skin-cells in order to make them resemble pluripotent stem-cells. These "IPS cells" are important because they provide pluripotent stem-cells for research, without the use of embryos. Also, because they are developed from a patient's own cells, future treatments might avoid rejection.

STEM CELLS AND DRUG TESTING

StemBANCC, was formed in 2012 to build a collection of induced pluripotent stem cell (**IPS**) cell lines for drug screening for a variety of diseases. Based at the University of Oxford, it brings together funding from 10 pharmaceutical companies and 23 universities with the aim of creating a library of 1,500 IPS cell lines which will be used in early drug testing by providing a simulated human disease environment.

EMBRYONIC VERSUS ADULT CELLS

Those who object to embryonic stem-cells will often suggest that adult stem cells or IPS cells offer at least as much potential for treatments as embryonic cells, but without the need to destroy human embryos. Others still believe that embryonic stem-cells offer some unique possibilities however. This debate is on-going and unresolved.

KEY TERMS

stem-cell - totipotent - multipotent - pluripotent - induced pluripotent cells - adult stem-cells - cytoplasmic embryo - chimera - embryonic stem-cell line - ontological difference - drug testing - cloning

SELF-ASSESSMENT QUESTIONS

1. What is a stem-cell?

2. Why are scientists so excited about stem-cell research?

3. "Research on stem-cells is immoral because it depends on the destruction of human lives". To what extent is this comment consistent with a Christian perspective, and is it reasonable?

4. "Creating human-animal hybrid embryos should be banned". Consider the arguments for and against such a ban before giving your own, reasoned response.

5. "There is no need to research embryonic stem cells anymore". Do you agree? Why?

6. Explain the Roman Catholic objection to embryo research.

7. Contrast a Kantian and a Utilitarian approach to stem-cell research.

8. How does the purpose of any stem cell research affect the ethics?

FURTHER READING

- **JONES, D.A**. - The Soul of the Embryo: An Enquiry into the Status of the Human Embryo in the Christian Tradition, Continuum 2004

- **HUENIN, L. M**. - The Morality of Embryo Use, CUP 2008

- **WARNOCK, M**. (ed.) - Question of Life: Warnock Report on Human Fertilization and Embryology, Wiley-Blackwell 1985

Genetic Engineering

The possibility of changing the genetic makeup of an embryo, foetus or even an adult has long fascinated scientists, offering the hope of a cure for genetic disorders. Sifting science fact from science fiction is not always easy.

GENE TRANSFER represents a relatively new possibility for the treatment of genetic disorders by changing the expression of a person's genes. Typically gene transfer uses a virus to deliver a new gene into target cells. The technique is not yet available outside clinical trials.

Gene transfer can be targeted to **SOMATIC** (body) or **GERM** (egg and sperm) cells.

- In **SOMATIC CELL GENE TRANSFER** the recipient's genome is changed, but the change is not passed on to the next generation.

- In **GERMLINE GENE TRANSFER**, the parents' egg and sperm cells are changed with the goal of passing on the changes to their children. This is not being researched, at least in larger animals and humans, although there is a great deal of discussion about its desirability.

Gene transfer was originally envisaged as a treatment of **MONOGENIC DISORDERS** (conditions which relate to a single faulty gene, such as Thalassemia, Sickle-cell Anaemia, Haemophilia, Cystic Fibrosis, Tay Sachs disease, Fragile X syndrome and Huntington's disease) but the majority of trials now involve the treatment of cancer, infectious diseases and vascular disease.

Human gene transfer raises several important ethical issues, in particular the potential use of genetic therapies for **GENETIC ENHANCEMENT** and the potential impact of germline gene transfer on **FUTURE GENERATIONS**.

Many people falsely assume that germline gene transfer is already routine.

Sometimes people confuse genetic selection as in **PREIMPLANTATION GENETIC DIAGNOSIS** (PGD) with genetic transfer, though in genetic selection no changes are made to the genes. It is important to realise that PGD is routinely being used to avoid implanting embryos with known genetic defects - as well as other undesirable qualities in terms of gender or appearance. The New Scientist reported that in 2012

> *"An American woman who is a carrier - which means she is healthy but at risk of passing the disease to her children - used standard genetic screening to select an embryo with low levels of faulty mitochondria. She also chose a male embryo."*

As long ago as 2001 scientists confirmed the birth of 30 genetically altered children following a procedure called **OOPLASMIC TRANSFER**. Doctors had injected some of the contents of a donor egg into an egg from a woman with infertility problems, resulting in an egg with two types of mitochondria. Technically, the 30 have **THREE GENETIC PARENTS**, since they carry a tiny amount of DNA from the donor. However, the gene transfer was an inadvertent side effect of the infertility procedure.

In the UK two similar procedures, offering parents with **MITOCHONDRIAL DISORDERS** such as Muscular Dystrophy the potential to conceive healthy children, were subject to an HFEA consultation which reported in March 2013. In a survey of 1000 people 56% said they were "very" or "fairly" positive about techniques which could prevent mitochondrial diseases, which affect 1 in 7000 children, by altering genetic make-up during IVF. A tenth were "very" or "fairly" negative and a third were undecided or unsure. The consultation will shortly be the basis for a bill which will aim to change the law so as to allow these treatments.

In March 2013 The New Scientist reported that

"Mitochondrial transfer is a form of "germ-line" genetic engineering, which is generally seen as unacceptably risky because it doesn't just alter the DNA of the child who receives it, but also that of future generations. For that reason we do not engineer out diseases like cystic fibrosis even though it is technically feasible to do so. Mitochondrial engineering is somewhat different, though. The mitochondrial genome is tiny, so the changes involved are minimal. The public seems to understand this".

SCIENTIFIC OBSTACLES

Viruses, while an effective means of introducing new genes into target cells, may also cause other problems such as toxicity, immune and inflammatory responses - and sometimes they affect more than just the target cells. Synthetic DNA might provide an alternative delivery-method and researchers are also experimenting with introducing a 47th chromosome to exist alongside the standard 46, presumably not affecting their functioning or causing mutations. An additional chromosome could carry substantial amounts of genetic code, and it is anticipated that the body's immune systems would not attack it.

It has been acknowledged that somatic gene transfer could lead to **INADVERTENT GERMLINE GENE TRANSFER**, because current technologies are far from precise. It is always possible that a virus might introduce the gene into a sperm cell rather than the target cell for example. If somatic gene transfer were to be conducted in utero there might be an increased likelihood that new genes might become part of the germline and be passed on to the foetus' children in due course.

INTENTIONAL GERMLINE GENE TRANSFER would involve the deliberate introduction of new genes into germ cells prior to fertilization with the aim of produce an embryo in which each and every cell carries the new gene and which will not pass on defects. Currently, this technology has not been applied to humans.

Animal studies have demonstrated difficulties with this technique. Some cells do not acquire the gene or acquire multiple or partial copies of the gene. It is not yet possible to control exactly where the new gene will be introduced, and some insertion locations may interfere with other genes. If these kinds of errors are detected, then embryos with these defects could be "selected out." However, should germline gene transfer be attempted in humans, it is likely that not all errors will be detected.

Germline gene transfer or somatic cell transfer in utero can often be more effective than somatic cell gene therapy used later in development. Nevertheless, this approach involves more risks.

- Children born with partial or multiple copies of a gene could be in a worse condition.

- Errors could lead to severe or even lethal complications

- Problems might not present straight away, even until after they have been passed on to future generations.

For these reasons, given the limits of current technology, germline gene transfer is not accepted by many scientists.

RELIGIOUS VIEWS

Most religious groups will find interference in human reproduction undesirable, even if it could lead to benefits for individuals and families. While few groups would issue blanket-bans on somatic-cell gene transfer, the risks involved to future generations in germline transfer would be a major source of concern and reassurance as to safeguards against unintentional germline transfer might be sought.

For Catholics and Evangelical Protestants any research which causes the destruction of embryos or which might directly contribute to the deaths of foetuses or children cannot be sanctioned. Anglican and more liberal protestant churches focus on the alternatives to heroic treatments, counselling couples to consider adoption or less extreme therapies and offering practical and emotional support as necessary. All Christian groups will express their sympathy and support for the parents and children affected by genetic disorders.

For Jewish communities genetic transfer offers a way of overcoming the Tay Sachs Disease (**TSD**), of which one in every 27 Jews in the USA as a carrier, and which leads to paralysis, dementia, blindness, psychoses, and eventually death. An individual must inherit two defective genes, one from each parent, to inherit TSD.

Over the past 25 years, screening and genetic counselling have greatly reduced the number of children born with TSD. Couples where one or both partners carry the TSD gene will be advised either to adopt children or to use IVF and PGD to avoid having a child who is either a carrier or affected by the disease. If women are already pregnant chlorionic villus sampling (**CVS**) or amniocentesis is offered at between 16 and 20 weeks to diagnose TSD before birth - if the test is positive then a termination may be offered. The tests in themselves carry a 1-4% chance of causing a miscarriage.

A great percentage of the babies born with TSD are now born to couples who were not previously thought to be at significant risk. In these cases clinical trials of somatic-cell gene transfer would offer a last chance of helping their children.

KEY TERMS

preimplantation Genetic Diagnosis (PGD) - ooplasmic transfer - mitochondrial Disorder - monogenic condition - somatic-cell gene transfer - germline gene transfer - genetic enhancement

SELF-ASSESSMENT QUESTIONS

1. What is the difference between PGD and Gene Transfer technologies?

2. Why do people often reject all Gene Transfer technologies?

3. How would Utilitarians and Situation Ethicists respond to the prospect of using germline therapies to eliminate Cystic Fybrosis and TSD?

4. "Germline Genetic Engineering should never be allowed!" Consider the arguments for and against this perspective, before giving your own reasoned response.

5. "According to the precautionary principle all research on Genetic Engineering should be halted. We cannot be sure that even animal research is safe and if we allow it the consequences will be dire…" Do you accept this argument? Why?

FURTHER READING

- **SALVESCU & BOSTROM** (eds) - Human Enhancement, OUP 2010

- **SANDEL, M.** - Case against Perfection: Ethics in the Age of

Genetic Engineering, Harvard University Press 2009

- **HARRIS, J.** - Enhancing Evolution: The Ethical Case for Making Better People, Princeton University Press 2010

- **BUCHANAN, A.** - Better than Human: The Promise and Perils of Enhancing Ourselves, OUP 2012

Euthanasia

Euthanasia comes from the Greek words for "a good death". It can be applied to a variety of different circumstances:

1. Historically, suicide to avoid dishonour was sometimes described as euthanasia.

2. A severely/terminally ill patient refusing further treatment and even food and water because they do not wish to face a long period of suffering.

3. Somebody writing a "living will", "advance directive" or **ADVANCE DECISION**, stating that they do not wish to be treated in case of a future crisis.

4. Assisted suicide (usually in the case of terminally ill people, tablets or a syringe is provided for a patient to use themselves, as happens at **DIGNITAS** in Switzerland).

5. A family doctor directly causing the peaceful death of a patient at their considered request (as Dignity in Dying and EXIT International campaign to make legal).

6. A family member or friend causing the death of somebody in what they judge to be that person's best interests, e.g. when they are in agony.

7. An intensive-care doctor switching life-support machines off, either at the request of the family or because it is judged to be in the patients' best interests.

8. GPs writing "do not resuscitate" (**DNR**) on a patient's medical notes, meaning that they will not be treated in a crisis, without consulting or informing the patient or their family members.

9. Consultants recommending the withdrawal of treatment, food and water from a patient who is judged to be close to death and not capable of making decisions about their own care (known as the **LIVERPOOL CARE PATHWAY** in UK hospitals).

10. A hospice nurse administering large doses of diamorphine to a patient, in the knowledge that it may shorten life, but with the primary intention of relieving intolerable pain.

Clearly, these situations are quite different so they are often referred to in terms of:

1. suicide

2. voluntary passive euthanasia

3. involuntary passive euthanasia

4. (physician) assisted suicide

5. voluntary active euthanasia

6. involuntary active euthanasia

7. non-voluntary active euthanasia

8. involuntary passive euthanasia

9. non-voluntary passive euthanasia

10. double effect

Ethically and legally, a distinction is usually made between things that are done to cause death, acts of commission **ACTIVE EUTHANASIA**, and things which are not done to cause death, acts of omission **PASSIVE EUTHANASIA**.

A distinction is also made between actions carried out by a person's choice **VOLUNTARY EUTHANASIA** and actions carried out on patients who are not consulted **INVOLUNTARY EUTHANASIA** or who cannot be consulted **NON-VOLUNTARY EUTHANASIA**.

The **PRINCIPLE OF DOUBLE EFFECT** is important, as it may allow treatments which shorten life when the primary intention is, for example, to relieve pain. This principle is widely recognised in ethical and legal discussions. The key lies in whether death was really a side-effect or whether it was part of the intention of the action.

THE LAW

Murder

Murder is illegal. In England and Wales, when a person:

- of sound mind and discretion (i.e. sane)

- unlawfully kills (i.e. not self-defence or other justified killing)

- any reasonable creature (human being)

- in being (born alive and breathing through its own lungs)

- under the Queen's Peace (i.e. not in war or under martial law)

- with intent to kill or cause grievous bodily harm

Then a murder has been committed. Where one or more of these conditions is not met then a homicide will usually result in a charge of manslaughter. For example, if the killer was mentally unbalanced at the time of the killing then it might be said to have been "manslaughter on the grounds of diminished responsibility".

Further, although Suicide was decriminalised in 1961, the Suicide Act stated that it is illegal to encourage or assist a suicide and that those who do may be sent to prison for up to fourteen years.

Since the Bland ruling of 1993, it is not illegal if a doctor omits to treat or even to nourish and hydrate a person who does not wish to live, or whose relatives or guardians reasonably deem that it is not in their best interests to live. However any act of commission, which directly causes the death of another person is illegal, even with consent.

Assisted suicide and all forms of active euthanasia are illegal in this country.

The right to die

Since the Human Rights Act was passed into UK law in 1998, campaigners have claimed that the denial of a right to release oneself from unbearable pain amounts to inhuman and degrading treatment (Article 3 of the European Convention on Human Rights), is a violation of privacy and family life (Article 8) and that an individual's inherent dignity and 'right to die' is violated by the current legislation. However, UK law does not recognise that a right to die is implied by the right to life. AC

Grayling, a patron of Dignity in Dying has said:

"I believe that decisions about the timing and manner of death belong to the individual as a human right. I believe it is wrong to withhold medical methods of terminating life painlessly and swiftly when an individual has a rational and clear-minded sustained wish to end his or her life."

Legal discrimination

Furthermore, for some campaigners, the legality of suicide in the UK suggests that sane, able-bodied person has the right to take their own life should they so wish, however the prohibition on any other person giving assistance effectively rules the disabled out of exercising this right. Campaigners suggest that this is discriminatory and that the disabled should be given assistance when they are unable to exercise their ultimate autonomy.

Other disabilities groups find the possibility that assisted suicide or euthanasia could be legalised profoundly threatening. In 2010 Not Dead Yet UK launched a resistance campaign, calling on all MPs to sign a charter declaring that they will support palliative care and independent living services and maintain legal protection for all people who are terminally ill or disabled. They see talk of a right to die as potentially undermining the right of the sick, elderly and disabled to live free from pressure to take their own lives.

Doctors often object to any "right to die" because it is to them that the responsibility of providing help falls. For many medical professionals causing a death is contrary to their Hippocratic Oath and otherwise unnecessarily confusing for those otherwise charged with doing good and not harming people. The shift from a beneficence model of medical ethics to an autonomy model, documented by Baroness O'Neill, has led to some doctors campaigning for Physician Assisted Suicide, but not many.

The existence of effective **PALLIATIVE CARE**, such as is practised within the **HOSPICE MOVEMENT**, is often seen as a third way, avoiding the need for active euthanasia. However, some campaigners doubt the efficacy of pain-relief and point to a **LACK OF DIGNITY** in enduring a prolonged death under the effect of strong drugs.

The doctrine of necessity

There are several defences to murder or assisting a suicide, but in the UK "necessity" is not one of them. 1n 1971 Lord Denning confirmed that the case-law governing this is still Regina v. Dudley & Stephens (1884).

Three castaway sailors decided to kill and eat a fourth. The court ruled that there was some degree of necessity arising from the threat of starvation but, at any moment one of them might have died naturally or a ship could have sailed over the horizon, so the defence of necessity could not stand.

In 2000, in the case of conjoined twins Jodie and Mary, doctors pleaded that it was **MEDICALLY NECESSARY** to operate, effectively killing one twin in order to save the other. This was allowed by Lord Justice Brooke because, unlike in Dudley & Stephens, doctors would not be selecting the victim.

The defence of medical necessity is currently restricted to cases where there are clashing duties, such as owed by doctors to different patients or by parents to their children. However, in 2012 Nicklinson v. Ministry of Justice tried to establish a defence of medical necessity for any doctor who helped somebody to die in an intolerable situation. This was denied and Tony Nicklinson died naturally of pneumonia as a complication of his "locked in syndrome", but his fight to get medical necessity accepted as a defence to murder in law, effectively allowing doctors to carry out voluntary active euthanasia, has been continued by Paul Lamb and others.

The lines between euthanasia, murder, manslaughter and assisted suicide are not clear and there have been several cases of people seeking **CLARIFICATION** in recent years, so that their relatives can be sure that they would not be prosecuted in the case that they helped a person to end their lives in some way.

In 2008 Debbie Purdy, who has Multiple Sclerosis, asked the Director of Public Prosecutions (DPP) for clarification of the law relating to assisted suicide so that her husband would not face prosecution if he helped her to travel to **DIGNITAS** in Switzerland to end her life if her condition became unbearable. Although the DPP was ordered to clarify the enforcement of the law in 2009, this has not really happened.

UK LAW REFORM

- An attempt to reform the law in England, allowing Voluntary Active Euthanasia, was made in 1936.

- In 1969, a Bill was introduced into the House of Lords by Lord Raglan.

- In 1970, the House of Commons debated the issue.

- In 1976 the utilitarian Baroness Wootton introduced a Bill to the Lords on passive euthanasia.

- Between 2003 and 2006 Lord Joel Joffe, a peer of Jewish descent, made four unsuccessful attempts to introduce bills that would have legalized assisted suicide and voluntary euthanasia, despite opinion polls recording 85% public support after a highly publicised seven hour debate.

- In 2008 the influential ethicist Baroness Warnock stated that pensioners in mental decline are "wasting people's lives" because of the care they require and should be allowed to opt for euthanasia even if they are not in pain. She insisted there was "nothing wrong" with people being helped to die for the sake of their loved ones or society, (Daily Telegraph, 28.6.13).

PRACTICAL PRESSURE

By 2026 experts predict there will be one million dementia sufferers in the country, costing the NHS an estimated £35 billion a year. Because of the scarcity in NHS resources, the ageing population, rising rates of cancer and dementia, the reduction in deaths from influenza and infections, euthanasia and assisted suicide are sure to be debated in parliament again before long.

RELIGIOUS TEACHING

Murder is condemned by all major religious traditions, as is suicide. **SUICIDE** is seen as self-murder. The Roman Catholic Church teaches that:

"Suicide is always as morally objectionable as murder. The Church's tradition has always rejected it as a gravely evil choice." (Evangelium Vitae, 66)

For Christians, Jews and Muslims life is the creation of God and therefore does not belong to us as individuals; it is not up to us to decide how and when our lives will end. That is God's prerogative.

Although several biblical figures reached rock-bottom and had suicidal thoughts ...

"I prefer strangling and death, rather than this body of mine. I despise my life; I would not live forever. Let me alone; my days have no meaning". (Job 7:15-16)

It is resignation and perseverance, submitting to God's will, however nonsensical and unfair it may seem, which is seen as the appropriate response in these situations. Yes, King Saul fell on his own sword in Battle, but he was not seen as a model of good behaviour. Similarly, Judas hanged himself after betraying Jesus and, although he is not explicitly condemned, few would see him as a role model (Matthew 27). The Bible teaches that **SUFFERING HAS MEANING AND VALUE**, it teaches us important lessons, and also gives those around us the opportunity to learn.

The Qur'an also teaches:

"do not kill yourselves [or one another]" 4:29

There is no specific scriptural teaching on euthanasia, nevertheless euthanasia involves taking human life and it is therefore rejected as contrary to the principle of the sanctity of human life, at least in its active forms.Nevertheless, some Christians, Jews and Muslims see this response as inappropriate when it means that terminally ill people are condemned to a prolonged and arguably undignified death.

Catholic scholars such as Richard Gula remind us that the Church does not require people to use extraordinary means to stay alive, but accepts that people may refuse treatments which prolong a life which has become **BURDENSOME** to them. The Papal Encyclical Evangelium Vitae (1995) records that:

> *"To forego extraordinary or disproportionate means is not the equivalent of suicide or euthanasia; it rather expresses acceptance of the human condition in the face of death."*

Nevertheless, the same document is clear that any

> *"action or omission which of itself and by intention causes death, with the purpose of eliminating all suffering"* is wrong, that *"euthanasia is a grave violation of the law of God, since it is the deliberate and morally unacceptable killing of a human person."*

Other groups of Christians, Jews and Muslims make a similar distinction between **ORDINARY** treatments and **EXTRAORDINARY** treatments, again stopping short of requiring people to undergo "heroic measures" to prolong life when there is little hope of that life being of a reasonable quality.

While this allows for voluntary passive euthanasia, it does not allow people to control the manner of their departure. Stopping treatment, while still being fed and hydrated, could still make for a prolonged and painful death - as in the cases of cancers or motor neurone disease. Some people feel that giving people the choice between continuing painful treatments or refusing treatments and slowly suffocating is not really a choice. It also condemns paralysed people to decades of solitary, motionless, **DEPENDENT** existence.

CASE STUDIES

In 1991 Dr Nigel Cox, who had been treating Lillian Boyes for 13 years for progressive rheumatoid arthritis, gave potassium chloride in her order to stop her heart. After she died, Patrick, one of her sons, thanked Cox; Boyes' suffering was appalling and she had pleaded with Cox repeatedly to end her life. Cox was arrested for attempted murder and later tried in 1992. He was given a 12-month suspended sentence, though Boyes' family supported his actions throughout the trial. He was also suspended for 18 months by the hospital, though he was allowed to teach at another hospital and continue his private practice. He was not struck off the GMC register.

In 1999 Dr David Moor, a GP from Northumberland, was prosecuted for the euthanasia of a patient. He was found not guilty despite admitting to having helped up to 300 people to die. The case for which he was tried was that of George Liddell, who was dying of cancer and was prescribed high doses of diamorphine by Dr Moor, after the last of which he died within 20 minutes. The broadcaster and euthanasia campaigner Ludovic Kennedy commented:

"Dr Moor should never have been tried - the whole trial was a complete waste of time and money ... He was only doing what

hundreds and hundreds of doctors do in this country every year.
The sooner the law is changed to allow doctors to legally help
people on their way, the better." (BBC News, 12.5.99)

DIGNITAS is a clinic in Zurich which allows people from overseas to have assisted suicide under Swiss Law. It has helped over 800 people to die, 60% Germans, with 180 from the UK.

- In 2008 Daniel James, aged 23, who had been paralysed in a rugby accident travelled to DIGNITAS with his parents to commit suicide.

- In 2009 the BBC's "A Short Stay in Switzerland" told the story of Dr Anne Turner, who had ended her life at DIGNITAS in 2006.

- In 2009, British conductor Sir Edward Downes and his wife Joan died "under circumstances of their own choosing." Sir Edward was not terminally ill, but his wife was diagnosed with rapidly developing cancer.

- In 2010, British comic-artist John Hicklenton ended his life following a 10-year battle with multiple sclerosis.

- In 2011 BBC2 aired "Terry Pratchett: Choosing to Die" in which pro-euthanasia Pratchett guided viewers through the assisted suicide of Peter Smedley, a British hotelier and millionaire, at the clinic.

Diane Pretty from Luton attempted to change the law, stating "I want to have a quick death without suffering, at home surrounded by my family" - through being assisted by her husband. Her Motor Neurone Disease had made it impossible for her to move or communicate easily, making her totally dependent, even though her mind was unaffected. Pretty used the Human Rights Act to argue that the Director of Public Prosecutions should make a commitment not to prosecute anybody involved in helping her to die. Her case, and a series of appeals, including to the European Court of Human Rights, failed. The Court rejected her argument that the right to life (Article 1 of the European Convention on Human Rights) included the right to die. She died naturally in 2002.

Non-Voluntary Euthanasia has become more of an issue since doctors have been able to keep people alive in intensive care units. The case of Tony Bland, who was put into a Persistent Vegetative State following injuries sustained in the Hillsborough Stadium disaster, established that doctors "need not strive officiously to keep patients alive" and enabled Bland to have feeding and water removed as well as treatment, allowing him to die quickly. Since 2006 there have been calls for clarification of the law governing the treatment of very premature infants, born and kept alive in the NICU but with no hope of recovery or a normal life.

AROUND THE WORLD

Voluntary Euthanasia or Assisted Suicide is allowed in Oregon (since 2000) in the Netherlands and Belgium (since 2002) Luxembourg (since 2008) and assisting a suicide for honourable motives has never been illegal in Switzerland.

Campaigners point to the growth in demand for these services over time and a corresponding diminution in hospice services and old-age-care, suggesting that concerns about a slippery slope might not be unfounded.

Nevertheless, in February 2013 France moved a step closer to legalising it, though a law has existed since 2005 authorising doctors to administer painkilling drugs at levels they know will, as a secondary effect, shorten a patient's life.

APPLYING ETHICAL THEORIES

Utilitarianism and Situation Ethics

It is clear that Situation Ethics and Proportionalism might support assisted suicide or voluntary euthanasia in cases of extreme, terminal suffering. The only concern would be the precedent that preferring death might set to others in similar situations, possibly suggesting to them that their lives are not worthwhile.

Most utilitarians, including preference utilitarians, would also allow most forms of euthanasia, as where a person has no more desire to live it cannot be in their interests to preserve their life. Peter Singer has been particularly vocal in support of euthanasia as a solution to the unjust distribution of scarce healthcare resources.

Kantian Ethics

Most AS Level answers will focus on Kant's comments on suicide in the Groundwork for the Metaphysics of Morals, suggesting that no form of Voluntary euthanasia could be allowed. Notwithstanding these comments, there is a possibility that Kantian thinking might justify euthanasia in some circumstances. As Allen Wood explained

> "In some places, Kant seems to be aware of (though never wholly to accept) the idea that suicide might be compatible with,

or even a necessary expression of, the preservation of our own dignity - when we face the prospect of a life deprived (by disease or by the mistreatment by others) of the conditions under which our human dignity can be maintained (MS 6:423, VA 7:258, VE 27:374)." (Duties to Oneself)

Christine Korsgaard writes

"Kant finds it obvious that committing suicide is treating yourself as a mere means, but if we understand the claim that humanity is valuable as the claim that it confers a normative standing, it is really not clear why this should be so. Why shouldn't a human being have the standing to confer value on her own demise, as well as on anything else she desires, provided that no other duty is breached?" (Valuing Our Humanity)

Further, in cases where a patient is in PVS or has no hope of resuming a free and rational life, it is only the potential precedent which helping them to die might set, the suppression of what might otherwise be useful sentiments, which would stand in the way of non-voluntary active euthanasia.

KEY TERMS

euthanasia - voluntary - involuntary - non-Voluntary - active - passive - principle of Double Effect - assisted suicide - palliative care - persistent vegetative state (PVS) - locked-in syndrome - non-maleficence - sanctity of life

SELF-ASSESSMENT QUESTIONS

1. What is Euthanasia?

2. "Christianity rejects all forms of Euthanasia" To what extent is this true?

3. "A new law on Euthanasia is necessary in the UK!" Do you agree? Explain your answer carefully, with reference to other perspectives.

4. Does palliative care make the need for euthanasia less?

5. Is it fair to say that legalising Physician Assisted Suicide would be the beginning of a slippery slope?

6. To what extent does Kantian Ethics prohibit euthanasia?

7. "The Catholic position on euthanasia is indefensible! It forces people to endure pointless agony for the sake of exerting its own authority!" Make a case for rejecting this statement.

8. A right to life implies a right to die! To what extent is this true?

9. Write a magazine article of 1000 words on DIGNITAS and the ethical debates it provokes.

10. Do you agree with Baroness Warnock, that mentally decaying pensioners have a duty to die? Why?

FURTHER READING

- **WILCOCKSON, M.** - Issues of Life and Death, Hodder 2009

- Your Ultimate Choice: Right to Die with Dignity (Voluntary Euthanasia Society), Souvenir Press (1992)

- **PITCHER, G.** - A Time to Live: The Case against Euthanasia and Assisted Suicide, ReadHowYouWant 2013

- **WARNOCK, M.** - Warnock and Elisabeth MacDonald "Easeful Death", OUP 2009

Bibliography

- **Chappell, T.** - Understanding Human Goods. Edinburgh: Edinburgh University Press, 1995

- **Denis, L.** - Abortion and Kant's Formula of Universal Law" ,Canadian Journal of Philosophy Vol. 37:4, 2007, pp. 547-580

- **Finnis, J.** - The Rights and Wrongs of Abortion: A Reply to Judith Thomson, Philosophy & Public Affairs Vol. 2, No. 2, 1973, pp. 117-145

- **Finnis, J.** - Natural Law and Natural Rights. Oxford: Oxford University Press, 1980

- **Finnis, J**. - Is Natural Law Theory Compatible with Limited Government?, Robert P. George (ed.) Natural Law, Liberalism, and Morality Oxford: Oxford University Press, 1996

- **Gensler, H.G.** - A Kantian Argument Against Abortion' , Philosophical Studies Vol. 49 (1986), p.83

- **Gillespie, N.** - Abortion and Human Rights, in Feinberg ed. The Problem of Abortion 2nd ed. Wadsworth, 1984,pp. 94-101

- **Hursthouse, R.** - Virtue Theory and Abortion, Philosophy & Public Affairs Vol. 20, No. 3, 1991, pp.223-246

- **Hare, R.M.** - A Kantian Approach to Abortion, Social Theory and Practice Vol. 15, Issue 1, 1989

- **Hare, R.M.** - Could Kant have been a Utilitarian?, Sorting Out Ethics Oxford: Oxford University Press, 1997

- **Korsgaard, C.** - Valuing our Humanity" , www.people.fas.harvard.edu

- **Mackie, J.L.** - Ethics, Penguin 1977, p227

- **McCoy, R.** - Kantian Moral Philosophy and the Morality of Abortion, Coe College, 2011

- **Parfit , D.** - Personal Identity, Philosophical Review; Vol. 80: 3-27, 1971.

- **Parfit, D.** - Reasons and Persons, Oxford: Clarendon Press, 1984

- **Parfit, D.** - Normativity, in Russ Shafer-Landau (ed.), Oxford Studies inMetaethics, Vol. I, Oxford: Clarendon Press, 2006

- **Sen, A.** - Elements of a Theory of Human Rights, Philosophy and Public Affairs Fall 2004; Vol.32:4, p315

- **Sensen, O.** - Kant on Human Dignity, Walter de Gruyter, 2011

- **Singer, P.** - Practical Ethics. 2nd ed. Cambridge: Cambridge University Press, 1993

- **Singer, P.** - Rethinking Life and Death, Oxford: Oxford University Press, 1994 pp.190-206

- **Singer, P.** - Taking Humanism Beyond Speciesism, Free Inquiry Vol. 24, no. 6 (Oct/Nov 2004), pp. 19-21

- **Warren, M.** - On the Moral and Legal Status of Abortion, Monist 57:1, 1973, reprinted in Biomedical Ethics 4th ed. Mappes and DeGrazia, eds. New York: McGraw-Hill, 1996, pp. 434-440

- **Warren, M.** - Moral Status: Obligations to Persons, Oxford: Oxford University Press (2000)

- **Wood, A.** - Duties to Oneself, Duties of Respect to Others, 2004

For hyperlinks to internet articles please visit www.philosophicalinvestigations.co.uk

General Reading

- **VARDY, P. & C.** - Ethics Matters, SCM Press 2012
  A useful exploration of ethical theories, giving more depth than most A Level books, with short chapters on Abortion, IVF and Euthanasia as well.

- **WILCOCKSON, M.** - Medical Ethics, Hodder 2008
  A full guide to this area of applied ethics from the legendary Head of Philosophy at Eton College. Very detailed and useful, but still accessible.

- **GLOVER, J.** - Causing Death & Saving Lives, Penguin 1990
  Glover is a utilitarian philosopher from the University of London. In this classic book he explores a range of applied issues, including abortion and euthanasia from this perspective.

- **HARRIS, J.** - The Value of Life, Routledge 1985
  This is a classic work from a leading bio-ethicist, especially recommended for those considering medical degree.

- **SINGER, P.** - Practical Ethics (3rd Ed), CUP 2011
  You should really try to engage with Singer in his own words. This is the most comprehensive work, but there are other works which would do as well.

Postscript

Charlotte Vardy is an experienced teacher of Philosophy and RS; she tutored at the University of London for seven years following studies at the Universities of Oxford, Cambridge and London. Author of The Tablet Student Zone and co-author of Ethics Matters (2012) and God Matters (2013) for SCM Press and of the five Arguing for God DVDs, she organises and speaks at Candle Conferences' student events while also working as teacher-trainer and consultant for an examination board and for educational charities, both in the UK and overseas.

Students seeking fuller explanations and a bibliography should also consult the website which also contains exam tips and past questions listed by theme.

The author welcomes comments on this book and contributions to the website - details are to be found online at:

www.philosophicalinvestigations.co.uk